Pat Carson and Roy White

CCEA A2

PHYSICS QUESTIONS

COLOURPOINT
EDUCATIONAL

Published 2020 by Colourpoint Creative Limited

© 2020 Pat Carson, Roy White and
   Colourpoint Creative Ltd

ISBN: 978 1 78073 216 9

First Edition
First Impression

Layout and design: April Sky Design, Newtownards

Colourpoint Educational
An imprint of Colourpoint Creative Ltd
Colourpoint House
Jubilee Business Park
21 Jubilee Road
Newtownards
County Down
Northern Ireland
BT23 4YH

Tel: 028 9182 0505
E-mail: sales@colourpoint.co.uk
Web site: www.colourpoint.co.uk

The Authors

Roy White taught Physics to A level for over
30 years in Belfast. He works for an examining
body as Chair of Examiners for Double Award
Science, Principal Examiner for GCSE Physics and
Principal Examiner for A level Life and Health
Sciences. In addition to this text, he has been the
author or co-author of three successful books
supporting the work of science teachers in
Northern Ireland.

Pat Carson has been teaching Physics to A level for
over 30 years in Belfast and Londonderry. He
works for an examining body as Chief Examiner
for GCSE Physics. In addition to this text, he has
been co-author on a number of books supporting
the work of Physics teachers at AS and A2 level.

This book has been written to help students preparing
for the A2 Level Physics specification from CCEA.
While Colourpoint Creative Limited and the authors
have taken every care in its production, we are not able
to guarantee that the book is completely error-free.
Additionally, while the book has been written to closely
match the CCEA specification, it the responsibility of
each candidate to satisfy themselves that they have fully
met the requirements of the CCEA specification prior to
sitting an exam set by that body. For this reason, and
because specifications change with time, we strongly
advise every candidate to avail of a qualified teacher and
to check the contents of the most recent specification for
themselves prior to the exam. Colourpoint Creative
Limited cannot be held responsible for any errors or
omissions in this book or any consequences thereof.

Note: it is the responsibility of teachers and lecturers to
carry out an appropriate risk assessment when planning
any practical activity. Where it is appropriate, they
should consider reference to CLEAPPS guidance.

Contents

Unit 4.1 (A2 1)
Deformation of Solids

1. A spring has a total length of 15 cm when a force of 5 N is applied to it. When a force of 7 N is applied to the spring its total length is 19 cm.
   (a) Calculate the unstretched length of the spring.
   (b) Calculate the value of the spring constant k in the equation $F = kx$ where F is the applied force and x is the extension of the spring.
   (c) Calculate the strain energy stored in the spring when a force of 4 N is applied to the spring.

2. Two identical springs with a spring constant of 400 N m^{-1} are arranged as shown on the right. Calculate the total extension when a force of 20 N is applied to the end of the springs. Hint: the force of 20 N is applied to each spring.

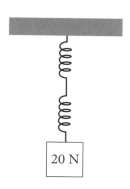

3. The springs used in question 2 are now arranged as shown on the right. Calculate the total extension when a force of 30 N is attached as shown. Hint: the force of 30 N is equally divided between the two springs.

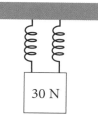

4. A steel wire is of original length 1.5 m and diameter 0.5 mm. One end of the wire is fixed and a force of 10 N is applied at the other end. The Young modulus of steel is 2.1×10^{11} Pa.
   (a) Calculate the extension of the wire.
   (b) Calculate the energy stored in the stretched wire.

5. A mass of 100.0 kg is suspended as shown on the right. One wire is made of steel, the other of brass. Each wire is 1.2 m long when the light rigid bar is horizontal. The bar remains horizontal as the wires stretch. The diameter of the steel wire is 0.5 mm. The Young modulus of steel is 2.1×10^{11} Pa, and the Young modulus of brass is 9.0×10^{10} Pa.
   (a) Calculate the tension in each wire.
   (b) Calculate the extension of the steel wire.
   (c) Calculate the diameter of the brass wire.

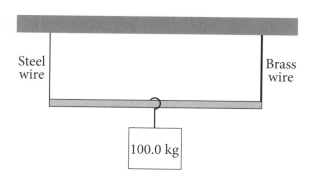

6. Two wires of negligible mass are arranged as shown in the diagram on the right. Weights are attached as shown. The lengths are those before the wires were stretched. The Young modulus of steel is 2.1×10^{11} Pa and the Young modulus of copper is 1.2×10^{11} Pa.
    (a) Calculate the extension of each wire.
    (b) Calculate the energy stored in the wires.

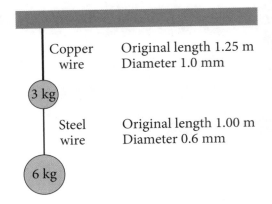

Copper wire — Original length 1.25 m, Diameter 1.0 mm

Steel wire — Original length 1.00 m, Diameter 0.6 mm

3 kg

6 kg

7. A wire was stretched. The force applied, F and the resulting extension, x are shown on the graph on the right. The original length of the wire was 2.5 m and its diameter was 0.4 mm.

    Using the graph and the values given, calculate the Young modulus of the material of the wire.

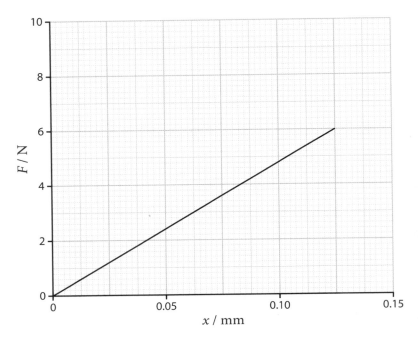

8. (a) Explain the difference between the limit of proportionality and the elastic limit.
    (b) Sketch a graph of stress (y-axis) against strain (x-axis) for a material that is stretched. On the graph mark the limit of proportionality and the elastic limit.

9. A concrete column of cross-sectional area 1.5 m² supports a force of 250 kN.
    The Young modulus of concrete is 3×10^{10} Pa.
    (a) Calculate the stress within the column.
    (b) Calculate the compression of the column if its unloaded length is 6 m.

10. The area of cross section of a steel wire is 0.025 cm².
    The unstretched length of the wire is 5.0 m.
    The Young modulus of steel is 2.1×10^{11} Pa.
    Calculate the work done in stretching the wire by 60 cm.

11. The stress/strain values for a material are shown in the graph on the right. Calculate the Young modulus of the material.

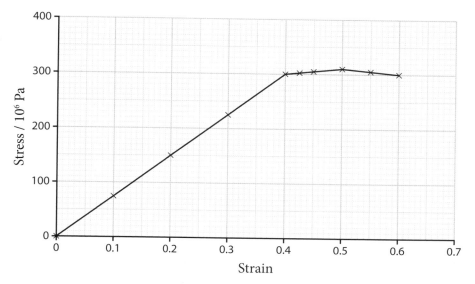

12. An aluminium wire has a length of 0.55 m and a diameter of 0.15 mm. It is stretched by 1.2 mm. The Young modulus of aluminium is 7.0×10^{10} Pa. Calculate:
    (a) the strain in the wire,
    (b) the stress in the wire,
    (c) the area of cross section of the wire,
    (d) the tension in the wire.

13. The graph on the right shows how the extension of a wire changed as increasing loads were placed on it. The original length of the wire was 5.0 m and its diameter was 4.0×10^{-4} m.

    Calculate:
    (a) the stress when the load is 40 N,
    (b) the energy stored in the wire when the load is 40 N,
    (c) the Young modulus of the material.

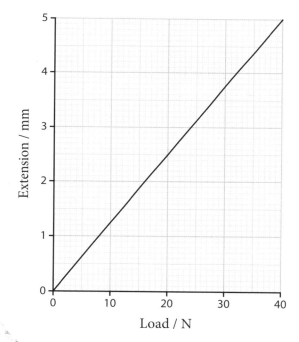

14. The force/extension graph for a wire is shown below.
     The original length of the wire is 1.6 m and it has a diameter of 1.2 mm.
     The wire broke at point **A** on the graph.
     (a) Calculate the stress in the wire when the wire broke.
     (b) Estimate the work done in stretching the wire until it broke.

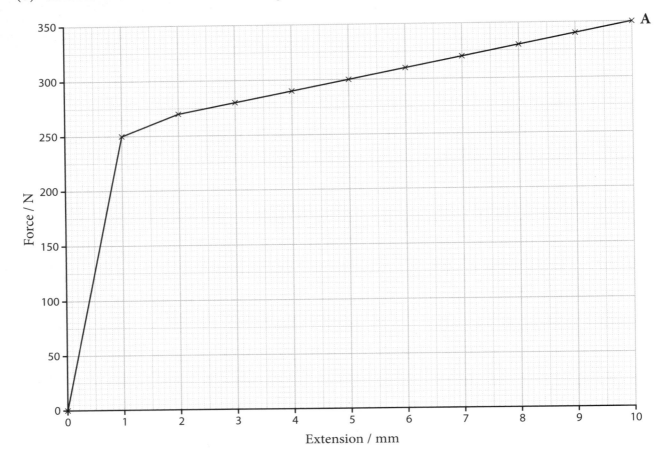

15. Two spring are arranged as shown in the diagram on the right. The
     spring constant of wire A is 4 N mm^{-1}, and that of wire **B** is 5 N mm^{-1}.
     A stretching force of 2.5 N is applied as shown.
     (a) By how much does each spring extend?
     (b) Calculate the spring constant for the combination of springs.

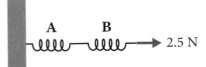

Unit 4.2 (A2 1)
Thermal Physics

1. Calculate the volume of 1 mol of any gas at STP.
   STP means a temperature of 273 K and a pressure of 1.01×10^5 Pa.

2. A container of molecular oxygen (O_2) at 50 °C and a pressure of 1.5×10^5 Pa has a volume of 6 m³.
   Calculate the mass of oxygen in the container.
   1 mol of O_2 has a mass of 32 g.

3. An experiment to study the effect of pressure on the volume of a gas was carried out using the J-tube apparatus shown on the right. The atmospheric pressure was 1.01×10^5 Pa.

   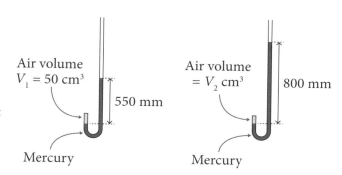

   The pressure due to a column of mercury is given by:
   pressure, $p = hrg$
   where:
   > h = height of the mercury column, in m
   > r = density of mercury, 13 600 kg m⁻³
   > g = acceleration of free fall, 9.81 m s⁻²

   The experiment is repeated for two heights of mercury, as shown. Calculate the volume V_2.

4. A container of volume 3.6×10^{-2} m³ contains 2.5×10^{-2} kg of an ideal gas.
   The pressure in the container is 0.75×10^5 Pa and the temperature of the gas is 22 °C.
   (a) Calculate the number of gas molecules in the container.
   (b) Calculate the root mean square speed of the gas molecules.

5. Helium can be treated as an ideal gas. A sample of helium at 32 °C contains 2.5 mol of atoms.
   (a) What type of energy do the atoms of an ideal gas have?
   (b) Calculate the internal energy of the gas.

6. The apparatus shown on the right was used to measure the specific heat capacity of a metal. The following measurements were taken:

   > Mass of the metal block = 1200 g
   > Current = 2.5 A
   > Voltage = 10.0 V
   > Time the heater was on = 4 minutes
   > Initial temperature of the metal = 18.5 °C
   > Final temperature of the metal = 24.2 °C

   Calculate the specific heat capacity of the metal.

   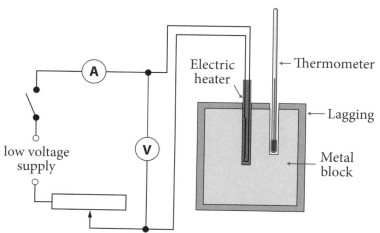

7. A metal is heated in a bunsen flame as shown on the right.
    The metal is heated to a temperature of 600 °C.
    It is then transferred to a beaker of water.
    The following measurements were taken:

    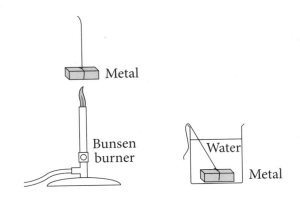

    Mass of the metal = 0.5 kg
    Mass of water in the beaker = 0.85 kg
    Initial temperature of the water = 15 °C
    Final temperature of the water and metal = 65 °C

    The specific heat capacity of water = 4200 J kg^{-1} K^{-1}.
    Calculate the specific heat capacity of the metal.

8. A gas has a pressure, p and a volume, V at a temperature of 20 °C. The pressure is tripled at a constant
    volume. What is the final temperature of the gas? Give your answer in kelvins.

9. Using the kinetic theory, explain the following observations.
    (a) When the volume of a gas is increased, the pressure it exerts decreases.
    (b) When the temperature of a gas is increased, the pressure it exerts increases.
    (c) When a gas is heated at constant pressure, it expands.

10. A car tyre is filled with air. The pressure gauge reads 210 kPa at 15 °C.
    When driven for a time the temperature of the air rises to 40 °C.
    Calculate the pressure of the air in the tyre now.

11. A Boyle's Law experiment was carried out at two different
    temperatures.
    The same mass of gas was used in each case.
    The graphs obtained are shown on the right.

    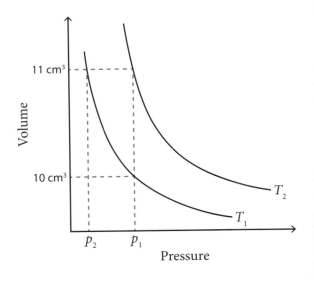

    Pressure p_1 = 1.2×10^5 Pa.
    Temperature T_1 = 288 K.

    (a) Calculate the number of moles of gas used in the
        experiment.
    (b) Calculate the temperature T_2.
    (c) Calculate the pressure p_2.

12. What is the root mean square speed of air molecules of O_2 and N_2 at 18 °C?
    The mass of an O_2 molecule is 5.34×10^{-26} kg and the mass of an N_2 molecule is 4.68×10^{-26} kg.

13. A balloon is inflated with helium at room temperature, 20 °C. When fully inflated, the balloon is a sphere of radius 20 cm and the pressure of helium inside is 1.2×10^5 Pa.
Calculate the mass of helium needed to fully inflate the balloon.
The mass of an He atom is 6.65×10^{-27} kg.

14. Show that for two gases at the same temperature, the ratio of their root mean square speeds is equal to the inverse of the square roots of their masses.

15. In interstellar space, the density of matter is about 1 hydrogen atom per cm³.
The temperature in interstellar space is 2.7 K.
The mass of a hydrogen atom is 1.67×10^{-27} kg.
   (a) Calculate the root mean square speed of the hydrogen atoms.
   (b) Calculate the pressure of the interstellar gas.

Unit 4.3 (A2 1)
Uniform Circular Motion

1. A washing machine is running a spin cycle with a value of 900 revolutions per minute (rpm).
    (a) Calculate the angular velocity of the washing machine drum.
    The diameter of the drum is 44 cm.
    (b) Calculate the velocity of a point on the edge of the drum.

2. An object of mass m is swung in a circle as shown on the
    right. The angular velocity of the object is ω and the radius
    of the circle is r. The tension in the string attached to the
    object is T.
    (a) Write down the relationship between the tension and
         the centripetal force.
    (b) Explain why the object can never be made to move in a
         horizontal circle.

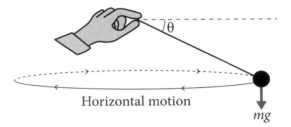

Horizontal motion

3. The Moon's orbit around the Earth is almost circular with an average radius of 3.8×10^8 m. The Moon's
    orbital period is 27.3 days, and its mass is 7.4×10^{22} kg.
    (a) Calculate the average angular velocity of the Moon.
    (b) Calculate the linear speed of the Moon as it orbits the Earth.
    (c) Calculate the magnitude of the centripetal force acting on the Moon.

4. A motorcyclist approaches a humpback bridge as
    shown. The radius of the bridge is 8 m.
    Calculate the maximum speed that the motorcyclist
    can pass over the bridge and still remain in contact
    with the road surface.

5. The diagram on the right shows a conical pendulum. The ball on
    the end of the string has a mass m and moves in a circle as shown.
    (a) Using the dimensions shown on the diagram calculate the
         value of the angle θ.
    (b) Write down an equation to show how the vertical component
         of the tension in the string, T, and the weight of the ball are
         related.
    (c) Write down an equation to show how the horizontal
         component of the tension in the string, T, and the centripetal
         force are related.
    (d) Using your answers to parts (b) and (c) calculate the angular
         velocity ω of the ball as it moves in its circular path.
    (e) Calculate the centripetal acceleration and tangential velocity of
         the ball.
    (f) Calculate how long it takes the ball to complete one revolution.
    (g) The ball has a mass of 0.5 kg. Calculate the tension, T, in the
         string.

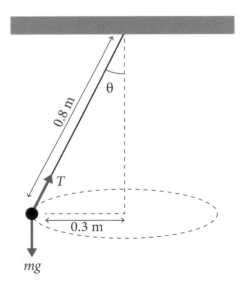

6. An object of mass 0.6 kg is moved in a vertical circle of radius 1.1 m. The object moves at a constant speed and completes one rotation in 1.5 s.
   (a) Copy the diagram on the right and mark the forces acting on the object at the four positions marked.
   (b) Calculate the tension in the string at each of the four positions.

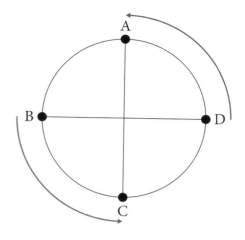

7. A ball bearing is released and allowed to roll down a track before performing a loop, as shown in the diagram.
   Derive the relationship between the height, H and the radius, r if the ball bearing is just to remain in contact with the track at the top of the loop.

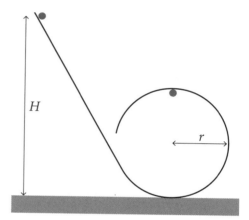

8. A coin of mass 6.5 g is placed on a rotating turntable as shown on the right. The angular velocity of the turntable is 0.2π rad s^{-1}.
   (a) How long does it take the turntable to complete one rotation?
   The angular velocity of the turntable is gradually increased and when it reaches a value of 0.6π rad s^{-1} the coin slides off the turntable at a tangent.
   (b) Calculate the maximum value of the frictional force between the coin and the turntable.

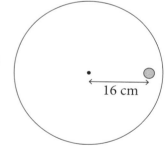

9. The passengers in a fair ground roll down the track into a dip as shown on the right. The radius of the circular track is 6.0 m. At what speed do they have to move in order to feel 2.5 times their normal weight?

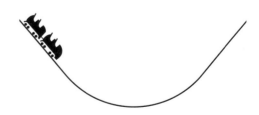

10. The equation used to calculate centripetal force is $F = \dfrac{mv^2}{r}$
    Show that each side of the equation has the same SI base units.

13

11. In order to produce a force that resembles gravity on a space station, it must rotate horizontally. The space station shown on the right has a radius of 20 m. What period of rotation is needed if it is simulate a force equal to 0.5g?

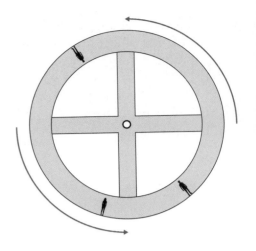

12. A mass, *m* connected to another mass, *M* by a string is made to move in a horizontal circle on a frictionless table as shown in the diagram. When the mass *m* is moving at a certain speed the mass *M* remains at rest. Derive the relationship between the tangential velocity, *v* and the quantities *M, m* and *r*.

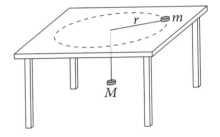

13. In the Bohr model of the hydrogen atom an electron revolves around the proton in a circular orbit of radius 5.3×10^{-11} m. The electron completes 6.6×10^{15} complete orbits in 1 second. The mass of the electron is 9.11×10^{-31} kg.
    (a) Calculate the tangential speed of the electron.
    (b) Calculate the centripetal force acting on the electron.

14. Roads are banked on curves so that a vehicle going around the curve at the recommended speed does not have to rely on the friction between its tyres and the road surface in order to pass round the curve. A cross section of a particular curve is shown on the right. The radius of the curve is 100 m and the recommended speed is 45 km hr^{-1}. The diagram on the right shows the forces acting on the car. At what angle θ should the curve be banked?

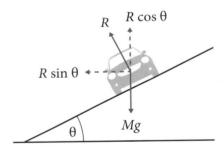

15. A wheel of radius 25 cm is rotating, taking 1.5 seconds to complete one revolution. Sketch graphs to show the angular velocity and tangential velocity at increasing distance from the centre of the wheel. Place relevant values on your graphs.

Unit 4.4 (A2 1)
Simple Harmonic Motion

1. A system is undergoing simple harmonic motion. At a time $t = 0.8$ s, the acceleration, a is $+0.58$ m s^{-2} and the displacement, x is -0.4 m.
    (a) Calculate the period of the motion.
    (b) Calculate the amplitude of the motion.

2. A mass hangs from a vertical spring, as shown in the diagram below. The mass is pulled down a distance of 5 cm and then released. It oscillates freely about an equilibrium position. The spring has a spring constant of 10.0 N m^{-1} and the mass has a value of 0.3 kg.

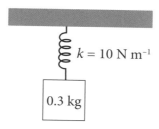

    (a) Calculate the period of oscillation.
    (b) Calculate the maximum acceleration of the mass.

3. The motion of an object moving back and forth with simple harmonic motion is a straight line. Its displacement, in metres, from the centre of oscillation varies with time according to the equation:

    $0.02 = 0.05 \cos 3.0t$

    (a) What is the amplitude of the motion?
    (b) What is the period of the motion?
    (c) Calculate the maximum acceleration of the object and state where this occurs.

4. A simple pendulum has a period of 1.6 s.
    (a) Calculate the length of the pendulum.
    (b) The pendulum bob is released as shown in the diagram on the right. The amplitude of the motion is 15 cm. Calculate the position of the bob, relative to its rest position, 0.6 s after release.

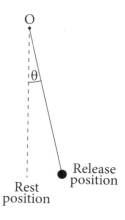

5. The graph below shows how the displacement of an object moving with simple harmonic motion varies with time.

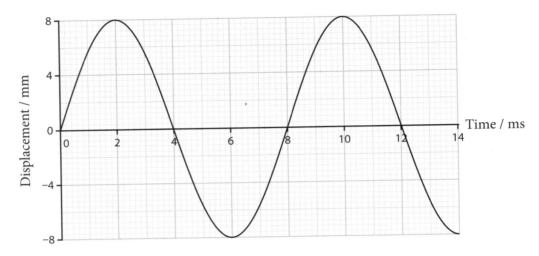

Using the graph, determine:
(a) the amplitude of the motion,
(b) the frequency of the motion,
(c) the maximum speed of the object.

6. An object of mass 2.0 kg rests on a platform, as shown on the right. The platform is attached to a system which makes the platform vibrate vertically with simple harmonic motion with an amplitude of 15 cm. At a particular frequency the object ceases for an instant not to be in contact with the platform. Calculate the frequency of the vibrating platform at which the object is no longer in contact with the platform and state the position at which this occurs.

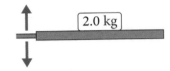

7. A mass of 0.1 kg is attached to the bottom of a spring, as shown on the right. The spring extends by 2 cm.
The spring is then pulled down another 2 cm and released.
(a) Calculate the frequency of oscillations of the mass-spring system.
(b) Calculate the maximum acceleration of the mass.

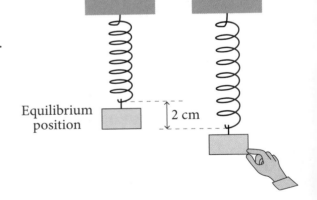

8. A mass-spring system has a period of 1.5 s and an amplitude of oscillation of 12 cm.
(a) Write down an equation which describes how the displacement of the mass on the end of the spring varies with time.
(b) What is the displacement of the mass 2.0 s after it has reached its lowest point? State its position relative to its equilibrium position.

9. A particle moves in a straight line, as shown on the right, with simple harmonic motion. It takes the particle 10 s to move from A to B.

    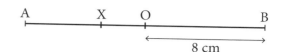

    (a) Calculate the period and frequency of the oscillation.
    (b) The particle reaches point X 2 seconds after passing through O from B to O. Calculate how far X is from O.

10. The period of a simple pendulum was measured as the length of the pendulum was changed. The results are shown in the table below.

Length of pendulum / m	0.2	0.4	0.6	0.8	1.0
Time for 10 oscillations / s	9.1	13.2	16.1	18.0	20.9

    Using the data above, plot a suitable linear graph and use it to find the acceleration of free fall, g.

11. Some oscillating systems are damped.
    (a) Explain what is meant by damping.
    (b) Sketch graphs to show how the amplitude and displacement of a damped oscillating system varies with time when it is:
    (i) lightly damped,
    (ii) critically damped.

12. (a) Explain what is meant by resonance in the case of an oscillating system.
    (b) State two effects that damping has on resonance.

13. A steel strip is clamped to a bench and a weight is attached to the other end of the strip, as shown on the right. The strip is then made to oscillate and a data logger is used to time the oscillations. Each time the strip passes through the data logger it records a time. The times are shown on the graph below.

    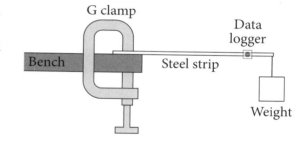

    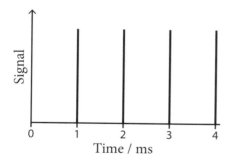

    (a) Calculate the frequency of oscillations of the steel strip.
    (b) The amplitude of the oscillations was measured and found to be 0.05 m. The oscillation of the strip is described by the equation:

    $x = A \cos \omega t$.

    State the meaning of the terms A and ω and write their values as they apply to the oscillation of the steep strip.

14. A mass is attached to a spring, as shown in the diagram. The spring is raised to position 1 and released. The diagram shows the position of the spring at five points in time during one oscillation.

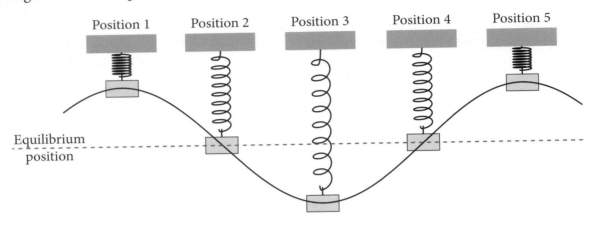

(a) At what position or positions is the displacement of the mass zero?
(b) At what position or positions does the mass have its maximum velocity?
(c) Describe the difference between the acceleration and displacement of the mass when it is at position 1 and position 3. Hint: Pay particular attention to the directions of these quantities in your answer.

15. The displacement, x of a particle moving with simple harmonic motion is given by the equation:

$x = 2.5 \cos (5.0t)$

where x is in metres and t in seconds.
(a) What is the amplitude of the motion?
(b) Calculate the frequency of the motion.
(c) Calculate the displacement when $t = 0.1$ s.

Unit 4.5 (A2 1)
The Nucleus

1. The diagram on the right shows the apparatus used in Rutherford's alpha-particle scattering experiment.
   (a) Identify each of the parts marked A to F.
   (b) Describe briefly how the measurements were made.
   (c) Why was it important to remove the air from the enclosure?

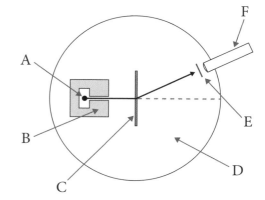

2. Copy and complete the diagrams on the right to show the paths that the alpha-particles would likely take through the two different models of the atom shown.

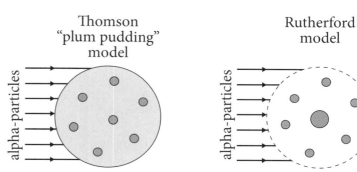

3. Outline how Rutherford's observations supported the following ideas about the atom:
   (a) That the nucleus was positively charged.
   (b) That, in comparison with the alpha-particle, the nucleus was much more massive.
   (c) That the atom was mostly empty space.

4. Hydrogen has three isotopes: hydrogen, deuterium and tritium.
   The notation for these nuclei is shown below.

hydrogen	deuterium	tritium
^1_1H	^2_1H	^3_1H

   Describe the nucleus of each isotope in terms of the particles they contain.

5. The nucleus of cobalt, chemical symbol Co, contains 27 protons and 32 neutrons.
   Write down the notation used to describe the composition of the nucleus of cobalt.

6. The results of many experiments have shown that the radius, r of a nucleus depends on its nucleon or mass number A. The relationship is described by the equation:

$r = r_o A^{1/3}$

What linear graph would you plot to obtain a value for r_o?

7. The mass of a nucleus, M contains A nucleons each of mass m.
   The density of nuclear material is ρ.
   Using the relationship for the volume of a sphere, obtain a relationship between the density, ρ, the mass of a nucleon, m and the radius, r, of the nucleus.

8. The table below shows the nuclear radius of a number of elements.

Nucleus	^{4}He	^{12}C	^{16}O	^{28}Si	^{32}S	^{40}Ca	^{51}V	^{59}Co	^{88}Sr
Radius, r / fm	2.08	3.04	3.41	3.92	4.12	4.54	4.63	4.94	5.34

The relationship between the number of nucleons, A and the nuclear radius, r is given by:

$r = kA^n$

Using the data provided in the table, plot a suitable linear graph and use it to find the values of k and n.

9. The radius of the nucleus of ^{14}C is 3.04×10^{-15} m.
   The mass of a nucleon can be taken as 1.67×10^{-27} kg.
   Calculate a value for nuclear density.

10. The value of $r_o = 1.2 \times 10^{-15}$ m.
    Calculate the radius of the nucleus of ^{238}U.

11. (a) Describe the structure of atom of $^{27}_{13}$Al in terms of protons, neutrons and electrons.
    (b) Calculate the radius of the nucleus of $^{27}_{13}$Al, taking $r_o = 1.2$ fm.

12. The mass of 1 mole of molecular hydrogen (H_2) is 2.016 g.
    (a) Calculate the mass of 1 atom of hydrogen.
    (b) Taking the density of nuclear matter to be 2.3×10^{17} kg m^{-3}, calculate the radius of the hydrogen nucleus (proton). Ignore the mass of the electron.

Unit 4.6 (A2 1)
Nuclear Decay

1. Copy and complete the decay equation below by writing the appropriate number in each of the three boxes.

$$ {}^{210}_{\square}\text{Po} \longrightarrow {}^{206}_{82}\text{Pb} + {}^{\square}_{\square}\text{He} $$

2. Complete the sentences below by identifying the missing word(s) in each case.

   (a) Beta-particles are very fast moving _____.

   (b) The relative charge of a beta-particles is _____.

   (c) Beta-particles can be stopped by a piece of _____ 2 mm thick.

3. The potassium isotope $^{42}_{19}\text{K}$ is radioactive and decays with the emission of a gamma ray (γ) to form the isotope of calcium $^{42}_{20}\text{Ca}$.

   (a) Write down the decay equation for this decay of $^{42}_{19}\text{K}$. Include any other radiation emitted besides the gamma ray.

   (b) The half-life of the potassium isotope is 12 hours. Calculate the decay constant of this potassium isotope. Give your answers in s^{-1}.

4. Radon-222 is a radioactive gas with a decay constant of 2.1×10^{-6} s^{-1}.
   The initial decay rate of a sample of the gas is 2.5×10^{6} Bq.
   Calculate the initial number of radioactive atoms present.

5. Protactinium has a half-life of 1.17 minutes.
   A sample of the substance has an initial of 1000 Bq.
   Calculate its activity after 50.0 s.

6. A radioactive sample has a half life of 51 days.
   Calculate the activity of the sample after one day.
   Initially the sample contained 8.0×10^{10} atoms.

7. Using the equation $A = A_0e^{-\lambda t}$ and the definition of the half-life, $t_{1/2}$ derive the relationship between the decay constant, λ and the half-life, $t_{1/2}$.

8. A sample of iodine-131 has a mass of 2.5×10^{-8} kg.
   One mole of iodine-131 has a mass of 0.131 kg.
   (a) Calculate the number of iodine atoms in the sample.
   (b) Iodine-131 has a half-life of 8 days. Calculate the decay constant, in s^{-1}, and the initial activity of the sample.

9. Technetium-99m is a radioisotope tracer used in nuclear medicine. The tracer has a half-life 6 hours.
   (a) Calculate the decay constant.
   (b) The tracer emits 140 keV gamma ray photons. Calculate the energy of these gamma ray photons, in joules.
   (c) The initial activity of the sample is 6×10^7 Bq. How long does it take for the amount of gamma ray energy to fall to 0.5×10^{-6} joules every second?

10. Carbon has radioactive isotope $^{14}_{6}C$ with a half life of 5730 years. This isotope is used in radiocarbon dating. In a sample of carbon only 1 atom in 10^{12} is of this radioactive isotope.
    A sample of 3 g of carbon taken from an archaeological site was found to have an activity of 0.05 Bq.
    (a) Calculate the decay constant of $^{14}_{6}C$ in s^{-1}.
    (b) What age does this activity of 0.05 Bq suggest for the archaeological site?
    $(1u = 1.66 \times 10^{-27}$ kg)

11. State the meaning of the three terms in the radioactive decay equation: $A = -\lambda N$.
    State the unit in each case.

12. One radioactive series begins with an isotope of uranium and end with an isotope of lead. Part of this series is shown below.

    $$^{238}_{92}U \xrightarrow{\alpha} Th \xrightarrow{\beta} Pa \xrightarrow{\beta} U \xrightarrow{5\alpha} Pb$$

    Draw a graph with the neutron number on the y-axis and the atomic (number of protons) on the x-axis. Mark each nucleus from the series on the graph. Using arrows mark and label the type of decay that takes place as each nucleus decays into another.

13. The isotope of iodine $^{131}_{53}I$ decays by beta emission to an isotope of xenon Xe*.
    The asterisk * indicates that this nucleus is in a excited state and decays by emitting a gamma ray.
    (a) Complete the decay equation for both the iodine and the xenon.
    (b) The half-life of iodine isotope is 8.04 days.
        Calculate the decay constant for iodine, giving your answer in s^{-1}.
    (c) The initial activity of a sample of the iodine isotope is 200 MBq.
        Calculate the number of iodine atoms in the sample.

14. To measure the half-life of the element protactinium the apparatus shown below is often used in school laboratories.

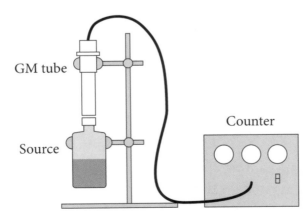

The activity of the source, in counts per second (cps), is recorded at regular intervals.
The measured activity is corrected for background.

(a) Explain what is meant by 'background', how it is measured and how it is used to correct the measured activity.

(b) The data from such an experiment is shown in the table below.

Time / s	0	20	40	60	80	100	120
Measured activity corrected for background / cps	500	410	337	276	226	186	152

Using the data from the table draw linear graph that will allow you to find the decay constant, in s^{-1}, and the half-life of protactinium.

Unit 4.7 (A2 1)
Nuclear Energy

1. Uranium-235 undergoes fission when its nucleus absorbs a neutron.
   (a) Write down an equation for the fission reaction shown in the diagram on the right.
   (b) Calculate the energy released by this reaction. Given your answer in MeV and in J.

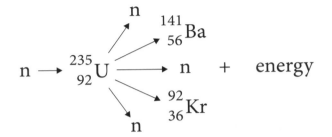

Mass of U-235 atom = 235.0439 u
Mass of Ba-141 atom = 140.9144 u
Mass of Kr-92 atom = 91.9262 u
Mass of a neutron = 1.0087 u

2. The mass defect for an isotope was found to be 0.410 u. Calculate the binding energy in kJ and in MeVs.

   $1\ u = 1.66 \times 10^{-27}$ kg
   $1\ MeV = 1.60 \times 10^{-13}$ J

3. Calculate the binding energy per nucleon (in units of MeV) for $^{9}_{4}$Be, for which the mass of the nucleus is 9.01219 u.

   Mass of a proton = 1.0073 u
   Mass of a neutron = 1.0087 u

4. The binding energy curve per nucleon is shown on the right.
   (a) Copy the curve, label each axis and place appropriate values on the axes.
   (b) Indicate which parts of the curve are appropriate for energy released by
      (i) fission,
      (ii) fusion.

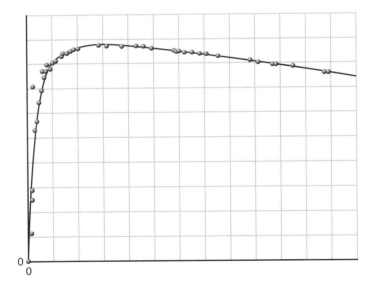

5. The nuclear fusion reaction shown below is one that could provide useful energy on the earth. Calculate the energy released. Give your answer in joules and MeV.

$$^2_1\text{H} + ^3_1\text{H} \longrightarrow ^4_2\text{He} + ^1_0\text{n} + \text{energy}$$

Mass of ^2_1H = 2.0141 u

Mass of ^3_1H = 3.0161 u

Mass of ^4_2He = 4.0026 u

Mass of ^1_0n = 1.0087 u

6. Nuclear fusion in the Sun involves what is termed the proton-proton cycle. A simplified version is shown below. Calculate the energy released at each stage by this reaction. Give your answer in joules and MeV.

1   $$^1_1\text{H} + ^1_1\text{H} \longrightarrow ^2_1\text{H}$$

2   $$^1_1\text{H} + ^2_1\text{H} \longrightarrow ^3_2\text{He}$$

3   $$^3_2\text{He} + ^3_2\text{He} \longrightarrow ^4_2\text{He} + ^1_1\text{H} + ^1_1\text{H}$$

Mass of ^1_1H = 1.0079 u

Mass of ^2_1H = 2.0141 u

Mass of ^3_2He = 3.0160 u

Mass of ^4_2He = 4.0026 u

7. Calculate the energy equivalent to 1 atomic mass unit.
1 atomic mass unit = 1.66×10^{-27} kg.

8. A neutron can decay into a proton, electron and an anti-neutrino, as shown below.

$$^1_0\text{n} \longrightarrow ^1_1\text{p} + ^0_{-1}\text{e} + \bar{\upsilon}$$

Calculate the energy released in this reaction. Ignore the effect of the anti-neutrino.

Mass of a proton   = 1.007277 u
Mass of a neutron   = 1.008665 u
Mass of an electron = 0.000549 u

9. An example of alpha particle decay is shown below.

$$^{238}_{92}U \longrightarrow ^{234}_{90}Th + ^{4}_{2}He$$

Calculate the energy released in this reaction.

Mass of U-238 = 238.050786 u
Mass of Th-234 = 234.043583 u
Mass of He   = 4.002603 u

10. When an electron and a positron meet they annihilate each other and produce gamma rays, as shown below.

$$^{0}_{-1}e + ^{0}_{+1}e \longrightarrow \gamma + \gamma$$

Calculate the total energy of the two gamma rays produced.

Mass of the electron = 0.0005486 u
Electrons and positrons have the same mass.

11. An electron is accelerated so that it gains 1.5×10^3 eV. Calculate its increase in mass and what this increase represents as a percentage of the electron's rest mass.

1 eV = 1 electron volt = 1.6×10^{-19} J
Rest mass of the electron = 9.1×10^{-31} kg

12. In July 1945, the first atomic bomb using the fission of plutonium was detonated in the United States. It produced 84 TJ of energy. The bomb used 6 kg of plutonium. Calculate the mass of plutonium converted to energy.

1 TJ = 1 terra joule = 1.0×10^{12} J

13. The largest thermonuclear bomb ever exploded was equivalent to 50 million tonnes of TNT and released 210 PJ. It required approximately 300 kg of hydrogen as the fuel for the fusion reaction. Calculate the actual mass of hydrogen that was converted to energy.

1 PJ is 1 Peta joule = 1.0×10^{15} J

Unit 4.8 (A2 1)
Nuclear Fission and Fusion

1. In the context of nuclear fission describe what is meant by the following:
   (a) Chain reaction,
   (b) Critical size,
   (c) Enrichment of the uranium fuel.

2. (a) Describe the role of the moderator in a nuclear fission reactor.
   (b) Neutrons released during a fission reaction have an energy of 1 MeV. To cause the fission of U-235 they are slowed by a series of collisions to an energy of less than 1 eV. After each collision their kinetic energy is 0.7 of their energy before the collision. Calculate the minimum number of collisions each neutron has before its energy is reduced from 1 MeV to just less than 1 eV.

3. The production of tritium is an important step in developing a nuclear fusion reactor. The equation below shows how this can be done using neutron capture by lithium. Copy and complete the equation by placing the correct figures in the boxes.

$$ {}^{6}_{3}\text{Li} + {}^{\square}_{\square}\text{n} \longrightarrow {}^{4}_{\square}\text{He} + {}^{\square}_{1}\text{H} $$

4. (a) What is ITER?
   (b) What is a plasma and how is it heated in this fusion reactor?
   (c) How is the plasma contained in the ITER reactor?

5. One method of plasma containment being investigated for use in nuclear fusion is inertial containment. Describe how inertial containment works.

6. The diagram below shows the main components of a nuclear fission reactor used to produce electricity.

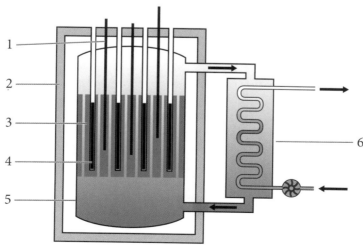

For each of the components numbered (1 – 6), state its name and write a brief description of its role in the operation of the reactor.

7. Nuclear fission can result in the production of various nuclei and differing numbers of neutrons. Four fission reactions are shown below.

$$^{235}_{92}U + {}^{1}_{0}n \rightarrow {}^{141}_{56}Ba + {}^{92}_{36}Kr + A{}^{1}_{0}n + energy$$

$$^{235}_{92}U + {}^{1}_{0}n \rightarrow {}^{142}_{54}Xe + {}^{B}_{38}Sr + 4{}^{1}_{0}n + energy$$

$$^{235}_{92}U + {}^{1}_{0}n \rightarrow {}^{139}_{C}Ba + {}^{94}_{36}Kr + 3{}^{1}_{0}n + energy$$

$$^{235}_{92}U + {}^{1}_{0}n \rightarrow {}^{D}_{55}Cs + {}^{90}_{37}Rb + 2{}^{1}_{0}n + energy$$

Determine the value of the letters **A**, **B**, **C** and **D**.

8. The use of nuclear power as a means of producing electricity continues to increase. The use of nuclear energy has both advantages and disadvantages. Write short notes outlining the following:
    (a) the environmental issues associated with nuclear energy;
    (b) the social issues associated with the location of a nuclear power station;
    (c) the dependability of supplies of uranium used in nuclear power stations.

9. In a fusion reactor, such as the one development in the ITER project, deuterium and tritium will fuse to form helium and a neutron and release energy. What form does this energy take and how could it be harnessed to generate electricity?

10. The nuclear fission of $^{235}_{92}U$ releases 203 MeV of energy. The nuclear fusion of $^{2}_{1}H$ and $^{3}_{1}H$ releases 17.6 MeV of energy. Using this information, show that the energy released per nucleon from fusion is greater than that from fission.

11. For two protons to combine during nuclear fusion they have to have sufficient kinetic energy to get to within 1.0×10^{-14} m of each other. The energy needed to overcome the repulsion is approximately 2.3×10^{-14} J. Using the Boltzmann relationship for the energy of a gas molecule, calculate the temperature required to provide the protons with this kinetic energy.

Units 5.1 and 5.2 (A2 2)
Force Fields
Gravitational Fields

In this section, take the value of the universal gravitational constant, G to be 6.67×10^{-11} N m^2 kg^{-2}.

1. Two identical metal spheres are in contact. Each sphere has a mass of 10 kg and a radius of 100 mm. Calculate the gravitational force between the two spheres.

2. A satellite of mass 200 kg orbits the Earth at a height of 36 000 km above the surface of the Earth. Assume the radius of the Earth is 6.4 Mm and its mass is 6.0×10^{24} kg.
   (a) Calculate the centripetal force on the satellite.
   (b) Calculate the numerical value of the gravitational field strength at this height.

3. A certain planet has a radius of 6.0 Mm. A mass of 5.00 kg on the surface of this planet has a weight of 49.0 N.
   (a) Calculate the mass of the planet.
   (b) Calculate the mean density of the planet, assuming it to be spherical.

4. Show that the unit for the universal gravitational constant can be expressed as m^3 kg^{-1} s^{-2}.

5. The Earth has a mass of 6.0×10^{24} kg and the Moon has a mass of 7.3×10^{22} kg. The distance between their centres of mass is 380 Mm. The Moon's mean radius is 1740 km.
   (a) Calculate the gravitational force between the Earth and the Moon.
   (b) Calculate the gravitational field strength on the Moon's surface.
   (c) At a certain point, P, between the Moon and the Earth, the force exerted on a mass by the Earth is numerically equal to that exerted by the Moon. Calculate the distance between the centre of the Earth and P.
   (d) Sketch a graph to show how the gravitational field strength varies with distance from the surface of the Earth to the surface of the Moon. Remember that the field strength changes direction at point P.
   (e) Using your answer to (d), suggest why it would require more fuel to travel from Earth to the Moon than to return from the Moon to Earth.

6. In the hydrogen atom, an electron orbits the nucleus at a fixed radius of 50 pm and at a constant speed of 2.2 Mm s^{-1}. Show that the gravitational force between the electron and the nucleus cannot provide the centripetal force. Assume the nucleus of the hydrogen atom consists of a single proton only.

7. The radius of the Earth is 6.4 Mm. The radius of Mars is 3.4 Mm. If the mass of the Earth is 9.5 times greater than that of Mars and the gravitational field strength at the surface of the Earth is 9.8 N kg^{-1}, show that the gravitational field strength on the surface of Mars is approximately 3.7 N kg^{-1}.

8. (a) Show that the mathematical form of Kepler's third law is consistent with Newton's law of universal gravitation.
   (b) The Earth has a mass of 5.98×10^{24} kg and the distance between the centres of mass of the Earth and the Moon is 385 Mm. Show that the orbital period of the Moon around the Earth is around 27.5 days.

9. The gravitational field strength on the surface of the Earth is approximately 9.8 N kg⁻¹. Calculate the gravitational field strength on the surface of another planet which has twice the mass and twice the radius of the Earth.

10. Assume that the planets orbit the Sun in circular paths at constant speed. Show that this speed is independent of the planet's mass.

11. Sputnik 1 was the first artificial Earth satellite. The Soviet Union launched it into orbit on 4 October 1957. Its period was 96.2 minutes. Calculate its orbital height assuming the mass of the Earth is approximately 6.00×10^{24} kg and its radius is 6.40×10^{6} m.

12. Astrophysicists believe that our Sun is in orbit around the centre of our Galaxy, the Milky Way, with a period of about 200 million years. It is generally thought that the distance between our Sun and the centre of the galaxy is about 1.6×10^{9} AU, where 1 AU (astronomical unit) is the mean distance between the Earth and the Sun. Assume that almost all of the mass of our galaxy is at the centre and calculate the number of times the mass of the Milky Way is greater than the mass of our Sun.

Unit 5.3 (A2 2)
Electric Fields

In this section, take the value of $\frac{1}{4\pi\varepsilon_0}$ to be 9×10^9 m F^{-1}.

1. Calculate the electrical force between an electron and a proton at a separation of 50 pm.

2. The most common unit for ε_0, the permittivity of free space, is C^2 N^{-1} m^{-2}. Show that the unit for the permittivity of free space can also be expressed as C V^{-1} m^{-1}.

3. ABC is an equilateral triangle of side 50 cm with point A at the apex. At B and C are stationary charges of magnitude +2 mC.
   (a) Calculate the magnitude and direction of the electric field at A.
   (b) State, without further calculation, the magnitude and direction of the force on a charge of +1 C now placed at A.

4. (a) Explain what is meant by a neutral point in the context of an electric field.
   (b) Explain why there can be no neutral point between two charges of opposite sign.
   (c) AC is a straight line of length 100 cm. There is a stationary charge of +2 mC at A. Calculate the size of the charge at C if there is a neutral point at B, where B is a point on the line AC at a distance of 40 cm from A.

5. Two hailstones are charged by friction. One has a charge of +40 µC and the other has a charge of –50 µC. Both hailstones have a mass of 9.0 grams.
   (a) State whether the force between the hailstones is attractive or repulsive.
   (b) Calculate the electrical force between the hailstones when they are 15 cm apart.
   (c) By what factor is the electrical force greater than the weight of one of the hailstones?

6. Two horizontal metal plates are placed 10 cm apart. The upper plate is at a potential of +5 V and the lower plate is at a potential of –5 V. A charged oil drop of mass 4.9×10^{-15} grams is at a point midway between the horizontal plates, moving vertically towards the upper plate at a constant speed. Ignore all resistive forces opposing motion and take g as 9.8 N kg^{-1}.
   (a) Calculate the magnitude of the electric field midway between the metal plates and state its direction.
   (b) Calculate the weight of the oil drop.
   (c) State the sign of the charge on the oil drop and give a reason for your answer.
   (d) State the size of the electrical force on the oil drop.
   (e) Using your answer to (a), calculate the charge on the oil drop.
   (f) Using your answer to (e), calculate the number of electron charges on the oil drop.
   The oil drop is now much closer to the upper plate.
   (g) Is the size of the upward force on the oil drop greater than, less than or equal to the value you calculated in part (d)?

7. What point charge at the centre of a sphere of radius 50 cm produces an electric field intensity at a point on the sphere's surface of 1 V m^{-1}?

8. Calculate the size of the constant electric field which can bring an electron moving at a speed of 5×10^6 m s^{-1} to rest in a distance of 60 mm.

9. The electric field strength, E, near a charged metal sphere is measured at different distances, r, from the centre of the sphere. The numerical values obtained are shown in the table.

Distance r / cm	32	40	48	64	72	80
E / kN C^{-1}	120	77	53	30	24	19

   (a) Plot the graph of E against $\frac{1}{r^2}$ and draw the straight line of best fit.
   (b) What conclusion can you draw from the graph?
   (c) Use the graph to estimate the charge distributed over the surface of the metal sphere.

10. Two parallel metal plates are arranged 10 cm apart and a potential difference of 500 V is maintained between them. A particle of dust weighing 3 fN and carrying a charge equivalent to 5 surplus electrons enters the field. Calculate the magnitude of the acceleration of the dust particle if the direction of the electrical force is:
    (a) vertically upwards,
    (b) vertically downwards,
    (c) horizontal.

11. Two point charges of +3 nC and +2 nC are placed 100 cm apart, as shown in the diagram below. Point A is 40 cm from the +2 nC charge.

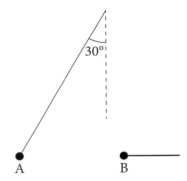

+3 nC   +2 nC   A

100 cm   40 cm

   (a) Calculate the size and direction of the electric field at A.
   (b) State one difference and one similarity between electric and gravitational fields.

12. A small metal sphere, A, carrying a charge of +3 nC is suspended by an insulated thread. Another small sphere, B, carrying a charge of +4 nC is brought close to A causing it to be repelled. When the spheres are 40 mm apart, the thread makes an angle of 30° to the vertical, as shown on the right. Calculate the weight of sphere A.

Unit 5.4 (A2 2)
Capacitors

1. (a) Describe, briefly, the construction of a capacitor.
    (b) Explain what is meant when it is said that the capacitance of a capacitor is 12 mF.

2. (a) When the potential difference across a capacitor is 12 V the charge stored on each plate is 120 µC.
        Calculate the capacitance of the capacitor.
    (b) What charge is stored in a 470 µF capacitor when the potential difference across its plates is 50 V?
    (c) What voltage exists across a 5 µF capacitor when it stores a charge of 150 µC?
    (d) Printed on an electrolytic capacitor is the following: "12 V, 2.2 µF".
        What information is the manufacturer giving the user of this capacitor?

3. (a) Show how you would connect three 4 mF capacitors together to form a network of capacitance
        (i)   1.33 mF
        (ii)   6.0 mF
        (iii) 2.67 mF
    (b) A physicist has an unlimited supply of capacitors all bearing the label "12 V, 2.2 mF". How could
        they construct a network of capacitance 2.2 mF capable of being charged to a potential of 36 V?

4. A 5 µF capacitor is charged and then disconnected from the electrical supply. During the next
    minute the potential difference across its plates fall by 6 V. Calculate the average leakage current
    between the plates.

5. A 6 mF capacitor is connected in parallel with a 3 mF capacitor. The combination is connected across a
    30 V supply. Calculate
    (a) the voltage across each capacitor,
    (b) the charge stored on each capacitor, and
    (c) the capacitance of the combination.

6. A 2.0 mF capacitor is charged by a 100 V supply and a 1.0 mF capacitor is charged by a 200 V supply.
    (a) Calculate the energy stored in each capacitor.
    The capacitors are then connected in parallel with each other, with like charges connected together.
    (b) Calculate the capacitance of the combination.
    (c) Calculate the total charge stored in the combined system of capacitors.
    (d) Calculate the new voltage across the combined system of capacitors.
    (e) Calculate the total electrical energy now stored in the combined system of capacitors.
    (f) Account fully for the difference in the answers to (a) and (e).

7. (a) A capacitor with capacitance C is discharged through a resistance R.
        Show that the product RC has units of time.
    (b) Sketch a graph of voltage against time for capacitor discharge and use it to explain what is meant by the time constant of a capacitor.
    (c) A capacitor of capacitance 10 µF is charged to a potential of 100 V. The capacitor is then discharged through a resistance of 5 MΩ.
        (i)   Calculate the time constant, τ.
        (ii)   After what time is the potential difference across the plates reduced to 50 V?
        (iii) Calculate the voltage across the capacitor's plates 80 seconds after the start of the discharge.

8. You are given a capacitor of capacitance around 20 mF, a fixed resistor of 5 MΩ, a 12 V battery and a double-pole single throw switch.
    (a) Draw a circuit diagram of the apparatus you would use to determine, as accurately as possible, the capacitance of the capacitor.
    (b) What additional apparatus would you need to carry out the experiment?
    (c) Describe what you would do and what measurements you would record.
    (d) How would you use your measurements to find the capacitance using a **linear** graph?

9. Defibrillators use capacitors designed for use in portable devices. A particular capacitor found in many defibrillators has a capacitance of 50 µF.
    (a) What charging potential difference would be required to store 100 J in a 50 µF capacitor?
    (b) Doctors need to be able to recharge the capacitor in the defibrillator in a time of 3 seconds. What average charging current is needed?
    (c) Calculate the mean charging power.

10. Electronic flash guns use an electric discharge in a gas such as xenon to produce an intense flash of light. In a particular flash gun a 47 µF capacitor supplies an average power of 15 000 W for 20 ms. What is the potential difference across the capacitor before it is discharged?

11. Three capacitors are connected in series across a 12 V battery. One has capacitance 4 µF and another has capacitance 12 µF. The capacitance of the third capacitor is unknown. The total energy stored in the three capacitors is 144 µJ. Calculate the capacitance of the unknown capacitor.

12. Two uncharged capacitors of 6 mF and 12 mF are connected in series across a 12 V battery.
    (a) Calculate the charge stored in each capacitor.
    (b) Calculate the voltage across each capacitor.

Unit 5.5 (A2 2)
Magnetic Fields

1. (a) What is a magnetic field?
    (b) Figure 1 shows a long, straight wire carrying a current, *I* in the direction indicated. Figure 2 is a plan view of the wire. The current is going into the page directly away from you. Copy figure 2 and on it sketch the magnetic field pattern associated with the current carrying wire.

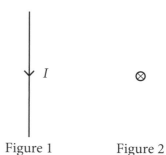

Figure 1   Figure 2

2. Two long thin wires carry a current in parallel directions as shown in the diagram on the right. Copy the diagram and on it mark:
    (a) the direction of the magnetic field at A due to the current in wire 1;
    (b) the direction of the force, if any, on wire 2, due to the current in wire 2;
    (c) the direction of the force on wire 1.

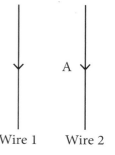

Wire 1   Wire 2

3. The diagram below shows part of an electric motor in which a current-carrying coil is placed in a magnetic field.

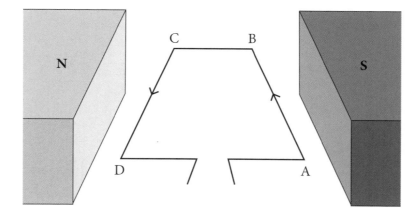

    (a) Copy the diagram and on it mark the direction of the force, if any, on sides AB, BC and CD.
    (b) In what direction will the coil rotate?

4. The diagram on the right shows a current carrying wire and a powerful magnet.

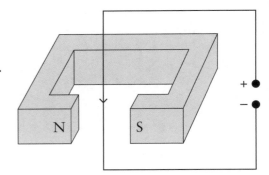

   (a) Copy the diagram and on it mark the directions of the magnetic field due to the magnet and the force on the wire.
   (b) When the current in the wire is 0.5 A and the length of the wire in the field is 10 cm, the force on the wire is 5 mN. Calculate the strength of the magnetic field due to the permanent magnet.
   (c) The current flowing in the wire is now doubled and its direction is changed so that it flows parallel to that of the magnetic field. What size is the force on the wire now?

5. A transformer has 3000 turns in its primary coil. It changes an AC of 240 V to 12 V. When a 60 W, 12 V lamp is connected across the secondary coil the lamp shines with normal brightness and a current of 0.26 A flows in the primary coil. Calculate:
   (a) the number of turns in the secondary coil;
   (b) the efficiency of the transformer.

6. A solenoid, X, is connected to a power supply unit, as shown below. A second solenoid, Y, is positioned very close to the first. Due to the changing voltage across X, the maximum flux density of 1.5 mT in Y repeatedly decreases linearly to zero in a time of 5 ms and then increases to 1.5 mT in the same time. The direction of the field in Y is always the same; only its magnitude is changing. The induced voltage in Y is observed on a CRO. Solenoid Y has an area of cross section of 0.006 m^2 and contains 2000 turns.

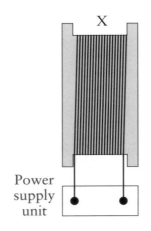
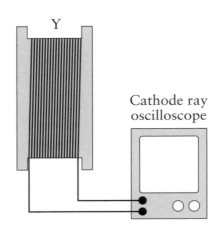

   (a) Calculate:
      (i) the maximum flux linked with solenoid Y;
      (ii) the electromotive force (e.m.f.) induced in solenoid Y.
   (b) Comment on the direction of the magnetic field due to the current in solenoid X and the direction of the magnetic field induced in solenoid Y at any instant in time.

7. State three ways in which practical transformers lose energy to the environment and describe briefly how good design can minimise these energy losses.

8. An AC generator consists of a rectangular coil of wire. The coil has many turns and it rotates at a constant frequency of 50 Hz about its axis in a uniform magnetic field. The output is a sinusoidal AC voltage of peak value 100π V. Calculate the maximum flux linkage with the coil and state when the flux linked with the coil is a maximum.

9. The 2800 turns of the secondary coil of a transformer are wound on the laminated iron core which has a cross-sectional area of 1.50×10^{-4} m². Calculate the change in magnetic flux density every second to cause 4.20 kV to be induced in the secondary coil of this transformer.

10. (a) By expressing both in terms of SI base units, show that the unit Wb s⁻¹ is equivalent to the volt.
    (b) A rectangular coil rotates at a constant angular velocity within a uniform magnetic field of strength 0.200 T. The coil has 400 turns and cross-sectional area 300 cm². The left diagram below shows the situation when the magnetic field is perpendicular to the plane of the coil. The right diagram shows the appearance of the coil viewed along the axis of rotation when the angle between the normal to the plane of the coil and the direction of the magnetic field, B is θ. The frequency of the rotation is 50.0 Hz.

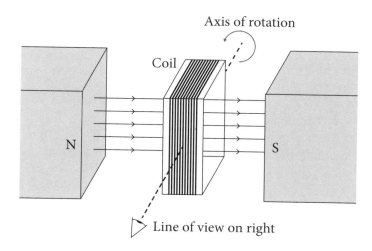

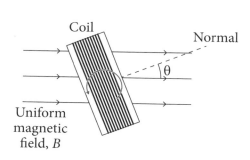

Calculate the following, giving each answer to 3 significant figures:
    (i)   the flux linked with the coil, Φ, when the angle θ is 60°;
    (ii) the time taken for the angle θ to change from 60° to 90°;
    (iii) the average rate of change of flux linked with the coil as θ rises from 60° to 90°;
    (iv) the average e.m.f. across the coil as θ rises from 60° to 90°.

11. (a) Describe how you could demonstrate qualitatively Faraday's law of electromagnetic induction using a coil, a selection of bar magnets of different strength and a centre-zero ammeter.
    (b) Describe how you could demonstrate Lenz's law using the same apparatus as in part (a). Illustrate Lenz's law with suitably labelled diagrams.

12. An iron-cored solenoid has 1000 turns of fine insulated copper wire. The magnetic field passing through the solenoid changes uniformly over a time of 5 seconds from 600 mT in one direction to 300 mT in the opposite direction. The cross-sectional area of the solenoid is 25 cm². The ends of the solenoid are connected to a voltmeter of internal resistance 9.0 Ω. Calculate:
    (a) Calculate how much charge is made to pass any cross section of the circuit in the 5 seconds in which the magnetic field is changing.
        Hint: Remember the induced current, $I = \dfrac{\Delta Q}{\Delta T}$.
    (b) Calculate the size of the average current in the external circuit.
    (c) Calculate the size of the instantaneous current when the magnetic field strength is zero.
    (d) State whether of not the direction of the current changes in the 5 second interval and explain your answer.

Unit 5.6 (A2 2)
Deflection of Charged Particles in Electric and Magnetic Fields

1. An electron moving at 3×10^6 m s^{-1} enters an evacuated space where there is an electric field of 120 V m^{-1} acting parallel to the direction of the electron's velocity. Calculate:
   (a) the force on the electron and state its direction;
   (b) the acceleration of the electron;
   (c) the time taken for the electron to come to rest;
   (d) the distance travelled by the electron in this time.

2. (a) A proton and a neutron are both moving at 2 Mm s^{-1} in a magnetic field of strength 2 T acting parallel to the particle's velocity. Find the force on each particle.
   (b) A proton is moving at 2 Mm s^{-1} when it enters a magnetic field of strength 200 mT acting perpendicular to the proton's velocity. Calculate the radius of the circle in which the proton now moves.

3. A proton, moving horizontally with a speed of 400 km s^{-1}, enters the uniform electric field between two horizontal metal plates, as shown in the diagram below. The electric field strength is 10 kN C^{-1} and its direction is vertically downwards. The potential difference between the plates is 800 V.

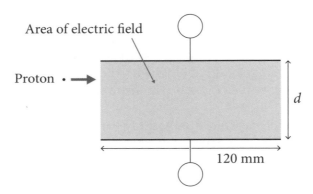

   (a) Copy the diagram and, in the circles, indicate the polarity of each plate.
   (b) Calculate the vertical distance, d, between the plates.
   (c) Calculate the magnitude and direction of the force and acceleration on the proton in the field.
   (d) Calculate the time spent by the proton in the field.
   (e) Calculate the vertical displacement of the proton at the point where it leaves the field.
   (f) On your copy of the diagram draw the trajectory of the proton.
   (g) Calculate the magnitude and direction of the proton's velocity at the point where it leaves the field.
   (h) State two ways in which the movement of the proton in this electric field is analogous to the movement of a projectile in a gravitational field.

4. A beam of charged particles moving horizontally with a speed of 5×10^5 m s^{-1} enters a uniform magnetic field perpendicular to their path, as shown in the diagram below. The beam of particles leaves the magnetic field travelling in a direction parallel to their initial velocity, but in the opposite direction. The beam has been vertically displaced by 40 mm as shown in the diagram.

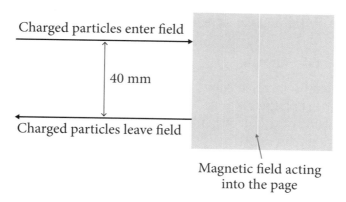

Charged particles enter field

40 mm

Charged particles leave field

Magnetic field acting
into the page

(a) State the sign of the charge on the particles.
(b) While inside the field the particles move in an arc of a circle. State the radius of this circular arc.
(c) If the strength of the uniform magnetic field is 0.142 mT, calculate the charge to mass ratio of the particles.
(d) Use your answers to parts (a) and (c) to identify the particles entering the field.

5. Electrons in a particular beam have velocities in the range 1 Mm s^{-1} to 10 Mm s^{-1}. As shown in the diagram below, they pass into the evacuated region between two vertical metal plates where there is a constant magnetic field of 200 mT.

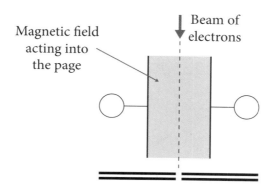

Magnetic field
acting into
the page

Beam of
electrons

(a) Copy the diagram, and mark on it the direction of the force on the electrons caused by this magnetic field.
(b) Calculate the maximum magnetic force on an electron in the beam.

An electric field is now switched on in the region between the plates. The polarity of the plates is such as to produce a force in the opposite direction to that produced by the magnetic field.
(c) On your copy of the diagram mark, in the circles, the polarity of the plates.
(d) State the magnitude of the electric force which would exactly cancel the force produced by the magnetic field on electrons moving at 5 Mm s^{-1}.
(e) The vertical plates are 8 cm apart. Calculate the voltage between the plates needed to produce the electric force found in part (d).
(f) Show that the ratio of the electric field, E, to the magnetic field, B, has units of m s^{-1}.
(g) Explain why only those electrons with velocity $v = \dfrac{E}{B}$ will pass through the region of the crossed fields in a straight line and pass through the defining slits below.

6. Electrons are accelerated from rest by a potential difference of 2000 V and then injected into a magnetic field of 2.0 mT at right angles to their path.
    (a) Calculate the kinetic energy and speed of the electrons as they move in their circular path in the magnetic field.
    (b) Calculate the centripetal force on the electrons.
    (c) Calculate the radius of the circle in which the electrons move.

7. Throughout this question take the value of $\frac{1}{4\pi\varepsilon_0}$ to be 9×10^9 N m^2 C^{-2}.

    In a hydrogen atom an electron an electron orbits a proton in a circular path of radius 52 pm.
    (a) State the source of the centripetal force.
    (b) Calculate the magnitude of the electric field strength due to the proton at a point on the electron's orbital path and state its direction.
    (c) Calculate the magnitude of the centripetal force.
    (d) Calculate the speed of the electron as it orbits the proton.

8. The diagram below shows a current, I, flowing through a metallic conductor. A magnetic field, B, causes the drifting electrons to be pushed to one side of the conductor and as a result a voltage is set up between opposite sides of the conductor. This is called the *Hall voltage* and it can be measured easily with a voltmeter. The width of the conductor across which the Hall voltage is measured is D.

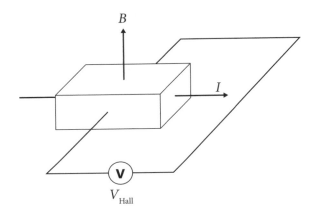

    (a) Copy the diagram and shade the face on which the electrons pushed sideways will accumulate.

    The Hall voltage, V_{Hall}, sets up an electric field. Electrons continue to be pushed sideways until the electrical force and the magnetic force on the electrons are equal in magnitude but opposite in direction, that is when equilibrium is reached.
    (b) Calculate the size of the electric field if V_{Hall} is 8 μV and the distance D is 2 cm.
    (c) Calculate the size of the electric force on an electron when V_{Hall} is 8 μV.
    (d) Calculate the speed of an electron in the middle of the conductor if the magnetic field is 0.4 T.

9. An electron moving with a speed of 2×10^6 m s^{-1} enters the magnetic field of a dwarf star. The direction of the electron's path is at 30° to the direction of the star's magnetic field direction. The strength of the star's field at that point is 500 mT.
    (a) Show that the component of the electron's velocity perpendicular to the field is 1.00×10^6 m s^{-1} and the component parallel to the field is approximately 1.73×10^6 m s^{-1}.
    (b) Use your answer to part (a) to show that the period of the circular motion of the electron caused by the interaction of the magnetic field and one of the components of its velocity is approximately 72 ps.
    (c) The other component of the electron's velocity causes it to spiral around the field line. The *pitch* is the separation of adjacent turns of the spiral measured along the field line. Show that the pitch of the spiral is approximately 0.12 mm.

10. An electron of charge e and mass m is injected into a magnetic field, B. Within the field the electron moves in a circular path at a constant speed, v.
    (a) Show that the period of its motion is $\dfrac{2\pi m}{Be}$.
    (b) Calculate the number of orbits made per second by an electron moving in a circular path within a magnetic field of strength 1 mT.

11. An electron moves in a magnetic field at a constant speed of 2×10^7 m s^{-1} in a circular path of radius 18 cm.
    (a) Calculate the strength of the magnetic field.
    (b) State what happens to the radius of the orbit as the strength of the magnetic field is slowly increased.
    (c) Describe and explain what happens to the electron's speed as the strength of the magnetic field is slowly increased.

12. In one form of mass spectrometer, singly-charged ions of different mass, but the same speed, enter a uniform magnetic field acting at right angles to their path. They then travel in a semicircle and are detected by a photographic plate. The arrangement is shown in the diagram below.

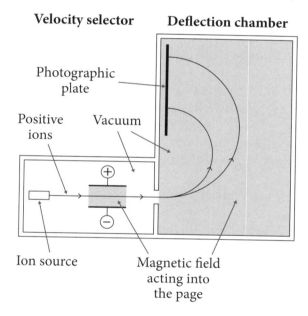

In one particular experiment, singly-charged barium-141 nuclei of mass 140.9577 u and singly-charged krypton-92 nuclei of mass 91.9264 u, each travelling at 2×10^5 m s^{-1}, enter the deflection chamber where a magnetic field of 0.8 T acts perpendicular to their path.
(a) Which nuclei travel in the semicircle of larger diameter?
(b) Taking 1 u as 1.66×10^{-27} kg, calculate the separation of the spots on the photographic plate caused by the impact of the different ion beams.

1. Describe the basic principles of operation of a synchrotron.

2. As particles are accelerated in a synchrotron, their mass changes in accordance with Einstein's Special Theory of Relativity.
   (a) In what way does the mass of a particle change as its speed approaches the speed of light?
   (b) How is this mass change dealt with in a synchrotron?

3. (a) What is antimatter?
   (b) How is antimatter produced on Earth?
   (c) Explain why antimatter cannot be stored for a long time on Earth.

4. Pair production is the creation of an elementary particle and its antiparticle, for example creating a muon and an antimuon. It can occur when a photon of sufficient energy comes very close to a heavy nucleus.
   (a) If a muon and an antimuon each have a rest mass 207 times greater than that of an electron, calculate the maximum wavelength of the single photon which can produce a muon and an antimuon together.
   (b) Suggest why it is necessary for a nucleus to be close for pair production to occur.

5. An electron and a positron collide and annihilate one another in a particle accelerator.
   (a) Explain why the annihilation can lead to the production of two gamma ray photons, but cannot lead to the production of a single gamma ray photon.
   (b) Calculate the wavelength of each of the gamma ray photons produced by annihilation of an electron with a positron.
   (c) Name three conservation laws which are obeyed in such an annihilation.

6. Copy and complete the table below to identify the four fundamental forces in order of their strength, their range and the gauge bosons (exchange particles) which mediate the forces. Some parts of the table have been completed for you.

	Force	Approximate range	Gauge boson
Weakest			Graviton
		1×10^{-18} m	
↓	Electromagnetic		
Strongest			

7. Hadrons and leptons are families of subatomic particles.
    (a) In what three ways are the hadrons and leptons different?
    (b) The hadron family is composed of the baryons and the mesons. In what way is the structure of a baryon different from that of a meson?
    (c) The familiar baryons are the proton and the neutron. State the quark structure of each of these particles.
    (d) Copy and complete the table below to show the properties of the up quark (u), the down quark (d) and their antiparticles.

Quark	Symbol	Charge / e	Baryon number, B
up	u	$+\frac{2}{3}$	
down	d		
anti-up	$\bar{u}$		
anti-down	$\bar{d}$		

    (e) In what types of interactions, if any, is baryon number not conserved?

8. (a) There are three generations (families) of leptons. One is the electron generation. What are the names of the other generations?
    (b) In what way, if at all, is there a trend in the mass of the leptons as one moves from one generation to the next?
    (c) Which neutrino (or antineutrino) do you associate with β^- decay?

9. (a) State the quark structure of a meson.
    (b) All of the mesons listed in the table below consist only of up quarks, down quarks and their corresponding antiparticles. Copy and complete the table to show the structure of the pions.

Particle	Structure	Charge / e	Baryon number, B
pi-zero, π^0	$u\,\bar{u}$		
pi-minus, π^-		-1	
pi-plus, π^+			

10. (a) An electron and a positron can annihilate (destroy) each other, in the following interaction:

$$e^- + e^+ \longrightarrow \gamma + \gamma$$

    (i)   Explain how lepton number is conserved in this interaction.
    (ii) State which force (strong, weak, gravitational or electromagnetic) is involved in this interaction, giving a reason for your answer.

    (b) In β^- decay a neutron changes into a proton and two particles are emitted from the decaying nucleus.
    (i)   Give the names of the particles which are emitted from the nucleus.
    (ii)   Identify the gauge boson which mediates the decay.
    (iii) Are lepton numbers conserved in β^- decay? Explain your reasoning.
    (iv)   Are baryon numbers conserved in β^- decay? Explain your reasoning.
    (v)   State which force (strong, weak, gravitational or electromagnetic) is involved in this interaction.

11. An isotope of lithium has an atomic number of 3 and an atomic mass number of 7. Consider a neutral atom of this isotope.
    (a) How many leptons does it contain?
    (b) How many baryons does it contain?
    (c) How many mesons does it contain?
    (d) How many up-quarks are in the nucleus of the atom?
    (e) What gauge boson mediates the force between the orbiting electrons and the nucleus?
    (f) What gauge boson mediates the force between the quarks in the protons and neutrons?

12. A particle physicist observes the following interaction between a proton and an unknown particle, **Y**, in which a neutron and a positron are produced.

    Y + p → n + e$^+$

    (a) State the charge on particle **Y**.
    (b) Neutrons and protons are baryons. State, with a reason, why the physicist can be confident that **Y** is not also a baryon.
    (c) Could **Y** be a lepton? Give a reason for your answer.
    (d) State the probable identity of **Y**.

Unit 6A (A2 3)
Practical Techniques

Examination Unit 3 is divided into two papers. The first, Unit 3A, is a practical examination consisting of two experiments, each lasing 30 minutes. Unit 3B is a one-hour paper on Data Analysis.

The skills required to do well in Unit 3A should not be underestimated. You must work quickly and methodically. You must use the skills learned over the whole A-level Physics course to carry out practical work, use apparatus appropriately and analyse experimental results.

There is only one way to prepare for Unit 3A – you must get practice in the laboratory doing practical work and analysing the data you collect. The five experiments which follow show the kind of experiment which you might be asked to do.

Experiment 1

The aim of this experiment is to find the value of an unknown resistor by measuring the ratio of currents.

Procedure
    (a)   Set up the electrical circuit shown below, but do not switch on the current.

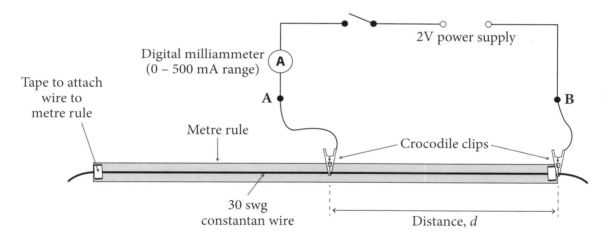

       (i)   Confirm with the teacher that the apparatus has been set up safely.
              (If you need help the teacher will build the circuit, but there will be a deduction of marks.)
      (ii)   Set the distance between the crocodile clips to be 350 mm.
     (iii) Switch on the power supply unit and, if necessary, the digital milliammeter.
     (iv) Record the reading on the digital milliammeter. This is the first value of I_1.
      (v)   Switch off the power supply unit.
    (b)   Using two leads, connect the fixed resistor mounted in a component holder between points **A** and **B** as shown in the circuit diagram on the following page.

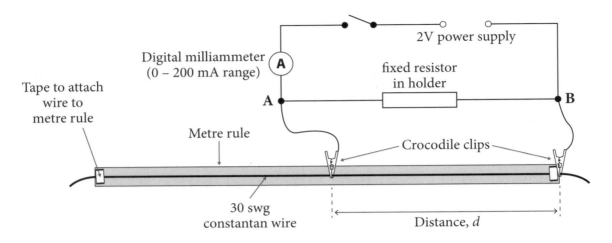

(i) Confirm with the teacher that the apparatus has been set up safely.
(If you need help the teacher will build the circuit, but there will be a deduction of marks.)

(ii) Close the switch and record the milliammeter reading I_2.

(iii) Switch off the power supply unit and disconnect the fixed resistor between **A** and **B**.

(iv) Increase the distance d by approximately 100 mm, by moving the appropriate crocodile clip to the left and repeat steps (a) and (b) until you have six sets of readings of d, I_1 and I_2. Record these results in a suitably-headed table.

Analysis

(c) (i) The ratio $\frac{I_2}{I_1}$ is related to the distance d by the equation:

$$\frac{I_2}{I_1} = 1 + \frac{k}{R}d^n \quad \text{where} \quad \begin{array}{l} k = \text{a constant, and} \\ R = \text{the resistance of the fixed resistor} \end{array}$$

Plot a suitable linear graph and use it to find the balue of n.

(ii) Calculate the value of R using values appropriate to $d = 450$ mm and $k = 0.027$ Ω mm^{-1}.

Experiment 2

The apparatus in the diagram on the right shows a pendulum suspended from a height, H above the floor of the laboratory. The distance between the pendulum bob and the floor is denoted by the letter h.

The aim of this experiment is to determine the distance, H, and the acceleration due to gravity, g, by measuring the period of oscillation of the pendulum for various distances, h.

The period of the pendulum, T, is given by the equation:

$$T = 2\pi \sqrt{\frac{H - h}{g}}$$

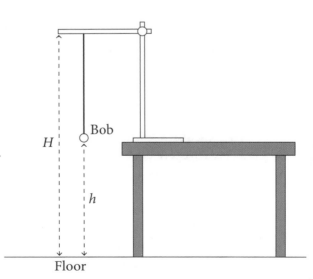

Procedure

(a) Measure and record in a suitable table the period of the pendulum for various heights, h, using the stopwatch provided. Your values of h should all be in the range 130 cm to 200 cm.

(b) Complete a table for 6 values of h in this range.

Analysis

(c) Use your data to plot an appropriate straight-line graph and use your graph to determine the value of H and a value for g.

Experiment 3

The aim of this experiment is to measure the focal length, f, of a lens. For various distances, D, you will locate the two positions of the lens which give sharp images on a white screen. You will then plot a straight line graph from which you will find the focal length of the lens.

You are provided with a lamp house, a white screen and a converging lens. The arrangement of the equipment is shown below. For any distance $D > 4f$, there are two positions of the lens which will produce a sharp image on the white screen.

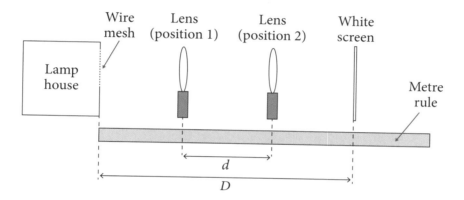

Procedure

(a) Place the screen initially at a distance of 650 mm from the lamp house.
  (i) Place the lens, in its holder, between the lamp house and the white screen, as close as possible to the lamp house.
  (ii) Move the lens until the first sharp image of the cross wires is seen on the screen.
  (iii) Record this initial position of the lens in an appropriate table.
  (iv) Move the lens further away from the lamp house until the second sharp image of the cross wires is seen and record this second position of the lens in a table.
  (v) Calculate and record the distance d between these two positions.
  (vi) Repeat for five further values of D between 65 cm and 90 cm.
(b) The mathematical relationship between D, d and f is:
  $$D^2 - d^2 = 4fD$$
  Draw a straight-line graph with $(D^2 - d^2)$ / cm^2 on the vertical axis, and $4fD$ / cm on the horizontal axis.
(c) Use your graph to determine a value for f.
(d) What is the uncertainty in your value for f?

Experiment 4

The aim of this experiment is to determine the time constant and capacitance of a charging capacitor.

Procedure

(a) (i) With the power supply unit (PSU) switched off, build the circuit shown on the right.

   (ii) Confirm with the teacher that the apparatus has been set up safely. (If you need help the teacher will build the circuit, but there will be a deduction of marks.)

(b) (ii) Switch the two-way switch to position Y and then turn on the PSU.

   (ii) Now switch the two-way switch to position X.

   (iii) Check that the initial reading on the microammeter is about 10 µA and that it slowly decreases, reaching around 5 µA after about 30 seconds.

   (iv) Switch off the PSU and discharge the capacitor by switching the two-way switch to position Y.

(c) (i) Switch on the PSU.

   (ii) Simultaneously start the stopwatch and switch the two way switch to position X.

   (iii) Record the current on the microammeter every 10 seconds over a period of 1 minute, entering the results in a copy of the table below.

   (iv) Repeat the procedure to obtain a second set of results.

   (v) Calculate the mean current at each time and complete the corresponding column in the table.

Time / s	First experiment Current / µA	Second experiment Current / µA	Mean current / µA
0			
10			
20			
30			
40			
50			
60			

Analysis

The current, I, in the charging capacitor changes with time according to the equation:

$$I = I_0 e^{-\frac{t}{\tau}}$$

where I = the current at time t,

         I_0 = the current at time $t = 0$, and

         τ = the time constant = $C \times R$

(d) Use your data to plot a suitable linear graph and use it to determine the value of the time constant, τ, of the charging capacitor.

(e) The resistor R has a resistance of 1×10^6 Ω. Determine the capacitance of the charging capacitor.

Experiment 5

The aims of this experiment are:
- to verify the potential divider formula by plotting a suitable graph;
- to measure the output voltage of a power supply unit, V_{in};
- to measure the resistance of an unknown resistor, R_2.

Procedure

Throughout this experiment you must not adjust the output voltage of the power supply.

(a) (i) You have been supplied with six fixed resistors. Five of them are labelled with the values of their resistance. The other resistor is labeled R_2.

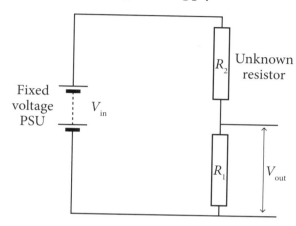

(ii) Ensuring that the power supply is switched off, build the circuit shown on the right, with R_1 being the 50 Ω resistor.

(iii) Connect the digital voltmeter across R_1 to enable you to measure V_{out}.

(iv) Confirm with the teacher that the circuit has been set up safely. (If you need help the teacher will build the circuit, but there will be a deduction of marks.)

(b) (i) Switch on the PSU and record in a suitable table the corresponding value of V_{out}.

(ii) Switch off the PSU and replace the 50 Ω resistor with the 100 Ω resistor.

(iii) Switch on the PSU and record in the table the corresponding value of V_{out}.

(iv) Continue in this way until five values of V_{out} have been obtained, one for each value of the resistors supplied.

Analysis

(c) The potential divider formula in your data sheet is shown below.

$$V_{out} = \frac{R_1 V_{in}}{R_1 + R_2}$$

Re-arrange the formula to give an equation in the form $y = mx + c$.

(d) Use your answer to part (c) to plot a straight-line graph that will allow you to determine the values of R_2 and V_{in}.

(e) Use your graph to determine the values of R_2 and V_{in}.

Unit 6B (A2 3)
Data Analysis

1. You are asked to carry out an experiment to determine the value of a capacitor.
   You are provided with the following:
   - four 1.5 V cells to build a 6.0 V battery,
   - two switches,
   - various connecting leads,
   - a digital microammeter,
   - a capacitor,
   - a resistor of value 80 kΩ.

   (a) Draw a circuit diagram, using all the apparatus listed, so that the capacitor can be charged in the shortest time possible and then discharged through the resistor.
   (b) The diagram below shows the screen of a digital microammeter. What is the current reading and what is its absolute uncertainty?

   The capacitor is charged and then discharged. The discharge current was measured every 10 seconds. The results are shown in the table below.

Time t / s	0	10	20	30	40	50	60
Current I / µA	75	38	21	12	7	4	2

   (c) Use the measurements to plot a linear graph and use it to determine the value of the capacitor.

2. When a ray of light passes through a rectangular glass block it is refracted towards the normal. When the ray emerges from the glass block it is refracted away from the normal. As a result, the path of the ray is displaced from its original path. Lateral displacement is the perpendicular distance between the incident ray and emergent ray as shown in the diagram.

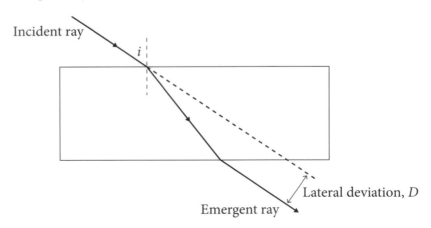

The lateral deviation, D was measured for a range of values of angle of incidence, i. The results are shown in the table below.

Angle of incidence, i / °	10	20	30	40	50	60	70	80	90
Lateral deviation, D / mm	3	6	10	14	19	25	33	41	50

(a) Using the data in the table plot a graph of the lateral deviation, D (on the y-axis) against the angle of incidence, i (on the x-axis). Label each axis with the quantity and its unit.

(b) Draw a curve of best fit through the points.

The best mathematical fit to this curve is as follows:

$D = 0.58 + 0.17i + 0.004i^2$

(c) Using angles of incidence of 30° and 60°, compare how closely this equation agrees with the measured values of D for these two angles of incidence. Express any difference as a percentage of the measured value.

3. The graph below shows how the displacement of a damped oscillating system changes with time. The co-ordinates of each point are shown on the graph.

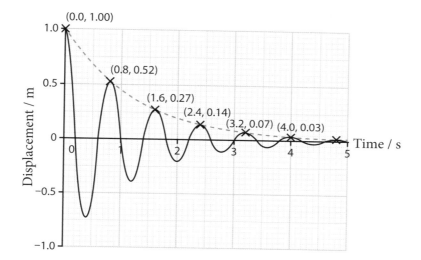

(a) Although the amplitude of the oscillations clearly decreases, the period remains the same. Explain how the graph supports this statement.

(b) Using data from the graph calculate the frequency of the oscillations.

(c) The dashed line shows how the amplitude, A decreases with time. This decrease in amplitude obeys the following equation:

$A = A_0 e^{-bt}$ where A_0 = the initial amplitude at time $t = 0$,
                    b = a constant, and
                    t = the time in seconds

Using values from the graph plot a linear graph from which the value of the constant b can be found. Hence determine the value of b.

4. The coefficient of restitution, symbol e, is a measure of how elastic a collision is. It is calculated using the following formula:

$$e = \frac{\text{kinetic energy after collision}}{\text{kinetic energy before collision}}$$

(a) (i)   What is the value of e for a perfectly elastic collision?
    (ii) What is the value of e for a totally inelastic collision?

The value of e can be measured in an experiment where a ball is dropped vertically from a measured height, H_0 as shown in the diagram on the left, below. The ball will bounce several times before coming to rest, as shown in the graph on the right, below. The total time, T that it takes to come to rest is measured. The height from which the ball is dropped is varied and, for each height, the total time, T is measured three times and an average calculated.

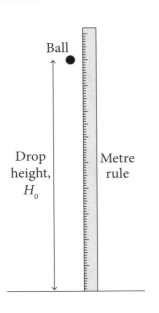

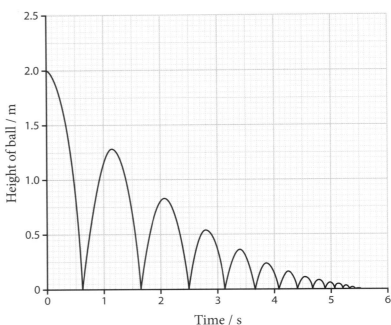

The total time, T_{total} is related to the height, H_0 from which the ball was released as shown by the following equation:

$$T_{total} = S H_0{}^m \qquad \text{where} \quad S = \text{a constant, and} \\ m = \text{a constant}$$

The ball is dropped from each height three times so that an average time for that height can be obtained. The results are shown in the table below.

Height H_0 / m	0.50	1.00	1.50	2.00	2.50
First time / s	2.75	4.10	5.05	5.80	6.40
Second time / s	2.85	4.05	5.15	5.70	6.45
Third time / s	2.90	4.00	5.10	5.75	6.35

(b) Calculate the average total time, T_{total} for each value of the height H_0.
(c) Plot a suitable linear graph from which the values of the constants S and m can be found, and hence find the values of S and m.
(d) Calculate the value for the coefficient of restitution, e from this data using the relationship:

$$S = \sqrt{\frac{2}{g}} \times \left(\frac{1 + e}{1 - e}\right)$$

Take $g = 9.81 \text{ m s}^{-2}$.

5. A radioactive source contains two radioactive elements, one an isotope of carbon and the other an isotope of sodium. The sodium isotope has a half-life of several years whilst that of carbon isotope is measured in seconds. The background activity was measured and the values below have taken this into account. The activity values are measured in MBq. Both radioactive substances have the same activity at time = 0. The activity of the source was measured every 10 seconds. The values are shown in the following table.

Time / s	0	10	20	30	40	50	60
Activity / MBq	4000	3400	2980	2680	2480	2330	2230

(a) Using the differences in the half-lives of each substance, extract from the data above the activity values for the carbon isotope.

(b) Use your data to obtain a linear graph from which the decay constant of the carbon can be found.

(c) Calculate the half-life of the carbon isotope.

6. If a material (for example, wood) is in the form of a beam the Young modulus of the material can be found by timing the oscillations of the loaded beam, as shown in the diagram below.

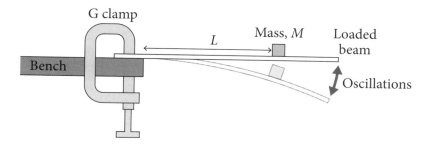

The period of oscillation, T is found by timing 20 oscillations as the distance, L to the position of the mass, M is varied. The results are shown below.

Length L / m	0.200	0.400	0.600	0.800	1.00
Time for 20 oscillations / s	8.0	22.0	42.0	64.0	90.0

(a) Using the data, plot a linear graph of T^2 (on the y-axis) against L^3 (on the x-axis). Draw a line of best fit through the points.

(b) Determine the gradient of the line.

(c) The Young modulus, E of the material is given by the equation:

$E = \dfrac{16\pi^2 M}{BD^3} \times$ (gradient of T^2 vs L^3)   where M = mass = (0.10 ± 0.001) kg
B = breadth of the beam = (0.050 ± 0.002) m
D = thickness of the beam = (0.010 ± 0.002) m

Calculate the value of the Young modulus, E of the material.

(d) Each measurement has an uncertainty associated with it. By expressing each uncertainty as a percentage, calculate the total percentage uncertainty in the value for Young modulus. Ignore the uncertainty in the gradient of your graph.

(e) Express this as an absolute uncertainty in the value of E.

Answers

4.1 Deformation of Solids

1. (a) When length = 15 cm, force = 5 N. When length = 19 cm, force = 7 N. So a force of 2 N causes an extension of 19 – 15 = 4 cm, and a force of 1 N causes an extension of 2 cm.
    Unstretched length = stretched length – extension = 15 – (5 × 2) = 5 cm
   (b) Use Hooke's Law: $F = kx$
    Substituting values: $5 = k \times 10$
    giving $k = 0.5$ N cm^{-1} = 50 N m^{-1}
   (c) A force of 4 N causes an extension of 4 × 2 = 8 cm or 0.08 m.
    Strain energy = $\frac{1}{2}kx^2 = \frac{1}{2} \times 50 \times 0.08^2 = 0.16$ J
    Note: To give the answer in joules the extension must be in metres and the spring constant must be in N m^{-1}.

2. Extension of one spring $x = 20 \div 400 = 0.05$ m.
   Total extension = sum of the two individual extensions = 2 × 0.05 = 0.10 m.

3. The force on each spring is 15 N. The extension $x = F \div k = 15 \div 400 = 0.0375$ (0.038) m

4. (a) Area of cross section $A = \pi d^2 \div 4 = 1.96 \times 10^{-7}$ m^2.
    Young modulus $E = \dfrac{\text{stress}}{\text{strain}} = \dfrac{F}{A} \div \dfrac{x}{l} = \dfrac{Fl}{Ax}$, so extension
    $x = \dfrac{Fl}{AE} = (10 \times 1.5) \div (1.96 \times 10^{-7} \times 2.1 \times 10^{11})$
    $= 3.64 \times 10^{-4}$ m (or 0.364 mm)
   (b) Energy = $\frac{1}{2}kx^2$. But spring constant $k = F \div x$, so
    Energy = $\frac{1}{2}Fx = \frac{1}{2} \times 10 \times 3.64 \times 10^{-4} = 0.0018$ J

5. (a) Tension in each wire = $\frac{1}{2}ma = \frac{1}{2} \times 100 \times 9.81$
    = 490.5 N
   (b) $x_{\text{steel}} = \dfrac{Fl}{A_{\text{steel}} E_{\text{steel}}}$
    $= (490.5 \times 1.2) \div (1.96 \times 10^{-7} \times 2.1 \times 10^{11})$
    $= 1.43 \times 10^{-2}$ m
   (c) If the rod is horizontal then:
    $x_{\text{brass}} = x_{\text{steel}} = 1.43 \times 10^{-2}$ m, so:
    $x_{\text{brass}} = 1.43 \times 10^{-2} = (490.5 \times 1.2) \div (A_{\text{brass}} \times 9 \times 10^9)$
    giving $A_{\text{brass}} = 4.57 \times 10^{-6}$ m^2
    $A_{\text{brass}} = \frac{1}{4}\pi d^2_{\text{brass}}$, giving $d_{\text{brass}} = 2.41 \times 10^{-3}$ m

6. (a) Re-arranging the equation for Young modulus gives the extension $x = \dfrac{Fl}{AE}$
    The force stretching the copper wire = (3 + 6) × 9.81 N.
    The force stretching the steel wire = 6 × 9.81 N

   For copper wire, $A = \pi d^2 = 7.85 \times 10^{-7}$ m^2
   So $x = (9 \times 9.81 \times 1.25) \div (7.85 \times 10^{-7} \times 1.2 \times 10^{11})$
   $= 1.17 \times 10^{-3}$ m extension in the copper wire.
   For steel wire, $A = \pi d^2 = 2.83 \times 10^{-7}$ m^2
   So $x = (6 \times 9.81 \times 1.0) \div (2.83 \times 10^{-7} \times 2.1 \times 10^{11})$
   $= 9.9 \times 10^{-4}$ m extension in the steel wire.
   (b) Energy is each wire = $\frac{1}{2}Fx$.
    For copper = $\frac{1}{2} \times 9 \times 9.81 \times 1.17 \times 10^{-3} = 5.16 \times 10^{-2}$ J
    For steel = $\frac{1}{2} \times 6 \times 9.81 \times 9.9 \times 10^{-4} = 2.91 \times 10^{-2}$ J
    Adding gives the total energy = 8.07×10^{-2} J

7. Area $A = \frac{1}{4}\pi d^2 = \frac{1}{4} \times 3.14 \times (0.4 \times 10^{-3})^2$
   $= 1.26 \times 10^{-7}$ m^2
   Take values from the graph: when $F = 6$ N, $e = 0.125$ mm = 0.125×10^{-3} m.
   Young modulus $E = \dfrac{Fl}{Ax}$, so:
   $E = (6 \times 2.5) \div (1.26 \times 10^{-7} \times 0.125 \times 10^{-3})$
   $= 9.52 \times 10^{11}$ Pa.

8. (a) When stretching a material, the limit of proportionality is the point beyond which Hooke's law is no longer true. The elastic limit is the point beyond which the material being stretched becomes permanently deformed so that the material does not return to its original length when the force is removed.
   (b)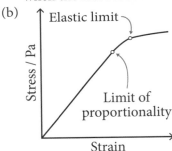

9. (a) Stress = force ÷ area = $250 \times 10^3 \div 1.5$
    $= 167 \times 10^3$ Pa
   (b) The compression is just the opposite of extension and is calculated in the same way.
    $x = \dfrac{Fl}{AE} = (250 \times 10^3 \times 6.0) \div (1.5 \times 3 \times 10^{10})$
    $= 3.3 \times 10^{-5}$ m

10. Re-arranging the equation for the Young modulus gives: $F = \dfrac{EAx}{l} = (2.1 \times 10^{11} \times 2.5 \times 10^{-6} \times 0.6) \div 5$
    $= 6.3 \times 10^4$ N
    Energy = $\frac{1}{2}Fx = \frac{1}{2} \times 6.3 \times 10^4 \times 0.6 = 1.89 \times 10^4$ J

11. Young modulus = stress ÷ strain = $300 \times 10^6 \div 0.4$
= 7.5×10^8 Pa

12. (a) Strain $\varepsilon = x \div l = 1.2 \times 10^{-3} \div 0.55 = 0.0022$
(b) Stress $\sigma = EA = 7.0 \times 10^{10} \times 0.0022 = 1.54 \times 10^8$ Pa
(c) Area $A = \frac{1}{4}\pi d^2 = 1.77 \times 10^{-8}$ m²
(d) Stress $\sigma = F \div A$, so: $1.54 \times 10^8 = F \div 1.77 \times 10^{-8}$
giving $F = 2.73$ N

13. (a) $A = \frac{1}{4}\pi d^2 = 1.26 \times 10^{-7}$ m²
Stress $\sigma = F \div A = 40 \div 1.26 \times 10^{-7} = 3.17 \times 10^8$ Pa
(b) Energy = $\frac{1}{2}Fx$ = area between the graph and the extension axis = $\frac{1}{2} \times 40 \times 5 \times 10^{-3} = 0.1$ J
(c) Strain $\varepsilon = x \div l = 5 \times 10^{-3} \div 5 = 1.0 \times 10^{-3}$
E = stress ÷ strain = $\sigma \div \varepsilon = 3.17 \times 10^8 \div 1.0 \times 10^{-3}$
= 3.17×10^{11} Pa

14. (a) Area of cross section $A = \frac{1}{4}\pi d^2$
= $\frac{1}{4} \times 3.14 \times (1.2 \times 10^{-3})^2 = 1.13 \times 10^{-6}$ m²
Stress at the breaking point = $F \div A$
= $350 \div 1.13 \times 10^{-6} = 3.1 \times 10^8$ Pa
(b) Work done = energy stored = area between the graph and the extension axis. To estimate the work done you will need to *estimate* this area.

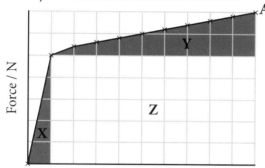

Area of X = $\frac{1}{2} \times 1 \times 10^{-3} \times 250 = 0.125$ J
Area of Y = $\frac{1}{2} \times 9 \times 10^{-3} \times 100 = 0.450$ J
Area of Z = $9 \times 10^{-3} \times 250 = 2.250$ J
So work done = $0.125 + 0.450 + 2.250 = 2.825$ J

15. (a) Using the Hooke's law relationship, $F = kx$, we get:
Spring A: $x_A = 2.5 \div 4 = 0.625$ mm
Spring B: $x_B = 2.5 \div 5 = 0.5$ mm
Total extension = $0.625 + 0.5 = 1.125$ mm
(b) $F = kx$, so: $2.5 = k_{comb} \times 1.125$
giving $k_{comb} = 2.22$ N mm⁻¹

4.2 Thermal Physics

1. $pV = nRT$, so: $1.01 \times 10^5 \times V = 1 \times 8.31 \times 273$
giving $V = 2.25 \times 10^{-2}$ m³
2. $pV = nRT$, so: $1.5 \times 10^5 \times 6 = n \times 8.31 \times 323$
giving $n = 3.35 \times 10^2$ moles
So mass = $3.35 \times 10^2 \times 32 = 1.07 \times 10^4$ g
3. Boyle's Law: $p_1 V_1 = p_2 V_2$
$p_1 = 1.01 \times 10^5 + 550 \times 10^{-3} \times 13\,600 \times 9.81$
= 1.74×10^5 Pa
$p_2 = 1.01 \times 10^5 + 800 \times 10^{-3} \times 13\,600 \times 9.81$
= 2.08×10^5 Pa
$1.74 \times 10^5 \times 50 = 2.08 \times 10^5\, V_2$, giving $V_2 = 41.8$ cm³

4. (a) $pV = NkT$, so:
$0.75 \times 10^5 \times 3.6 \times 10^{-2} = N \times 1.38 \times 10^{-23} \times 295$
giving $N = 6.63 \times 10^{23}$ molecules
(b) The mean kinetic energy of the gas molecules
= $\frac{3}{2}kT = 3.2 \times 1.38 \times 10^{-23} \times 295 = 6.11 \times 10^{-21}$ J
The mean kinetic energy of a gas molecule is also equal to $\frac{1}{2}m\langle c^2 \rangle$. So: $\frac{1}{2}m\langle c^2 \rangle = 6.11 \times 10^{-21}$
The mass of a molecule, $m = 2.5 \times 10^{-2} \div 6.63 \times 10^{23}$
= 3.77×10^{-26} kg, so $\langle c^2 \rangle = 3.24 \times 10^5$
Root mean square speed = $\sqrt{3.24 \times 10^5} = 569$ m s⁻¹

5. (a) Ideal gas molecules are pictured as solid spheres; they cannot rotate or vibrate; they only travel in straight lines. This is translational kinetic energy.
(b) 2.5 moles = $2.5 \times 6.02 \times 10^{23}$ atoms
Internal energy
= N × average kinetic energy of an atom
= $N \times (\frac{3}{2}kT)$
= $2.5 \times 6.02 \times 10^{23} \times \frac{3}{2} \times 1.38 \times 10^{-23} \times 305$
= 9.50×10^3 J

6. $Q = mc\Delta q$, $Q = IVt = 2.5 \times 10 \times 4 \times 60 = 6\,000$ J
$c = 6000 \div 1.2 \times 5.7 = 877$ J kg⁻¹ K⁻¹

7. Heat lost by the metal = heat gained by the water. So:
$0.5 \times c_{metal} \times (600 - 65) = 0.85 \times 4200 \times (65 - 15)$,
giving $c_{metal} = 667$ J kg⁻¹ K⁻¹

8. $p_1 V_1 \div T_1 = p_2 V_2 \div T_2$
So: $pV \div 293 = 3pV \div T_2$, so: $\frac{1}{293} = \frac{3}{T_2}$, and $T_2 = 879$ K

9. (a) As volume increases, the pressure decreases because there are fewer collisions per second with the container walls, since the gas particles have a greater distance to travel between their collisions with the walls.
(b) As the temperature increases, the pressure increases, because the molecules travel faster, have more collisions per second and each collision results in a greater momentum change. A greater momentum change per second means the rate of change of momentum has increased, so the force has increased, which in turn means the pressure has increased.
(c) To maintain the same pressure the number of collisions per second has to remain the same. Since the gas is being heated the particles are moving faster, therefore a greater distance to the container walls is needed.

10. $\frac{p_1}{T_1} = \frac{p_2}{T_2}$, so: $\frac{210}{288} = \frac{p_2}{313}$, giving $p_2 = 228$ kPa

11. (a) $pV = nRT$, so: $1.2 \times 10^5 \times 10 \times 10^{-6} = n \times 8.31 \times 288$
giving $n = 0.0005$ moles
(b) At p_1 (1.2×10^5 Pa) with a temperature T_2 the volume = 11 cm³. Using $pV = nRT$:
$1.2 \times 10^5 \times 11 \times 10^{-6} = 0.0005 \times 8.31 \times T_2$
giving $T_2 = 318$ K
(c) When $p_1 = 1.2 \times 10^5$, $V_1 = 10$ and $T_1 = 288$.
p_2 is unknown, $V_2 = 11$ and $T_2 = 288$.
$\frac{p_1 V_1}{T_1} = \frac{p_2 V_2}{T_2}$, so: $\frac{1.2 \times 10^5 \times 10}{288} = \frac{p_2 \times 10}{318}$,

giving $p_2 = 1.09 \times 10^5$ Pa

12. $\frac{1}{2}m\langle c^2 \rangle = \frac{3}{2}kT$. For O_2:

$\frac{1}{2} \times 5.34 \times 10^{-26} \times \langle c^2 \rangle = \frac{3}{2} \times 1.38 \times 10^{-23} \times 291$

so $\langle c^2 \rangle = 2.25 \times 10^5$, and hence r.m.s. speed = 475 m s^{-1}

For N_2:

$\frac{1}{2} \times 4.68 \times 10^{-26} \times \langle c^2 \rangle = \frac{3}{2} \times 1.38 \times 10^{-23} \times 291$

so $\langle c^2 \rangle = 2.58 \times 10^5$, and hence r.m.s. speed = 508 m s^{-1}

13. Volume of the balloon (sphere) = $\frac{4}{3}\pi r^3 = 0.0335$ m^3

$pV = nRT$, so: $1.2 \times 10^5 \times 0.0035 = n \times 8.31 \times 293$

n = number of moles = 1.65. Mass of helium

$= 1.65 \times 6.02 \times 10^{23} \times 6.65 \times 10^{-27} = 6.65 \times 10^{-3}$ kg

14. $\frac{1}{2}m_1\langle c_1^2 \rangle = \frac{3}{2}kT = \frac{1}{2}m_2\langle c_2^2 \rangle$

So: $\dfrac{m_1}{m_2} = \dfrac{\langle c_2^2 \rangle}{\langle c_1^2 \rangle}$ and therefore: $\dfrac{\sqrt{m_1}}{\sqrt{m_2}} = \dfrac{\sqrt{\langle c_2^2 \rangle}}{\sqrt{\langle c_1^2 \rangle}}$

15. (a) $\frac{1}{2}m\langle c^2 \rangle = \frac{3}{2}kT$, so:

$\frac{1}{2} \times 1.67 \times 10^{-27} \times \langle c^2 \rangle = \frac{3}{2} \times 1.38 \times 10^{-23} \times 2.7$

giving: $\langle c^2 \rangle = 6.693 \times 10^4$,

and hence: $\sqrt{\langle c^2 \rangle} = 258$ m s^{-1}

(b) $pV = \frac{1}{3}Nm\langle c^2 \rangle$, so: $p = Nm\langle c^2 \rangle \div 3V$

$= (1 \times 1.67 \times 10^{-27} \times 6.693 \times 10^4) \div (3 \times 1.0 \times 10^{-6})$

giving pressure, $p = 3.73 \times 10^{-23}$ Pa

4.3 Uniform Circular Motion

1. (a) 900 rpm = 900 ÷ 60 = 15 revolutions per second.
   Angular velocity $\omega = 2\pi \times 15 = 94.3$ rad s^{-1}.
   (b) $v = \omega r = 30\pi \times 0.22 = 21$ ms^{-1} (to 2 sig. fig.)

2. (a) $T \cos\theta = m\omega^2 r$
   (b) $T \sin\theta = mg$. If the string is horizontal $\theta = 0°$, so $T = mg \div 0$ = infinity. An infinitely large force is not possible, so the string can never be horizontal.

3. (a) $\omega = \dfrac{2\pi}{T} = 2\pi \div (27.3 \times 86400) = 2.66 \times 10^{-6}$ rad s^{-1}
   (b) $v = \omega r = 2.66 \times 10^{-6} \times 3.8 \times 10^8 = 1.01 \times 10^3$ m s^{-1}
   (c) $F = \dfrac{mv^2}{r}$ or $m\omega^2 r = 2 \times 10^{20}$ N.

4. $R - mg = \dfrac{mv^2}{r}$. When contact is lost with the road: $R = 0$ so $mg = \dfrac{mv^2}{r}$
   So $v = \sqrt{gr} = 8.9$ m

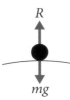

5. (a) $\sin\theta = 0.3 \div 0.8$, giving $\theta = 22°$
   (b) $T \cos 22° = mg$, giving: $0.927T = 9.81m$
   (c) $T \sin 22° = m\omega^2 r$, giving $0.375T = 0.3m\omega^2$
   (d) Take the ratio $\dfrac{0.927T}{0.375T} = \dfrac{9.81m}{0.3m\omega^2}$ giving
   $2.47 = \dfrac{32.7}{\omega^2}$. So $\omega^2 = 13.24$, and $\omega = 3.64$ rad s^{-1}.
   (e) $a = \omega^2 r = 3.64^2 \times 0.3 = 3.97$ m s^{-2}
   $v = \omega r = 3.64 \times 0.3 = 1.09$ m s^{-1}
   (f) Time for 1 revolution $= \dfrac{2\pi}{\omega} = \dfrac{2\pi}{3.64} = 1.73$ s
   (g) $0.927T = 9.81m$, so $T = \dfrac{9.81 \times 0.5}{0.927} = 5.29$ N

6. (a)

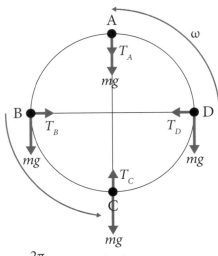

(b) $\omega = \dfrac{2\pi}{T} = 4.19$ rad s^{-1}.

$T_B = T_D = m\omega^2 r = 0.6 \times 4.19^2 \times 1.1 = 11.6$ N

$T_A + mg = m\omega^2 r$, $T_A = 11.6 - 0.6 \times 9.81 = 5.70$ N

$T_C - mg = m\omega^2 r$, $T_C = 11.6 + 5.9 = 17.5$ N

7. At the top of the circle
   $R - mg = \dfrac{mv^2}{r}$
   When contact is lost,
   $R = 0$ so $mg = \dfrac{mv_{min}^2}{r}$
   and hence $v_{min}^2 = gr$
   Apply the Principle of Conservation of Energy:

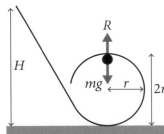

Loss of GPE = KE at the top of the circle, so:

$(mgH - 2mgr) = \frac{1}{2}mv_{min}^2$

giving $v_{min}^2 = 2(gH - 4gr)$.

But $v_{min}^2 = gr$, so: $gr = 2gH - 4gr$, giving $5gr = 2gH$

so $H = 2.5r$

8. (a) $\omega = 0.2\pi = \dfrac{2\pi}{T}$, giving $T = 2\pi \div 0.2\pi = 10$ s.
   (b) $F = m\omega^2 r = 6.5 \times 10^{-3} \times (0.6\pi)^2 \times 0.16 = 3.7 \times 10^{-3}$ N

9. $R - mg = \dfrac{mv^2}{r}$, so: $2.5mg - mg = \dfrac{mv^2}{r}$
   giving $2.5g - g = \dfrac{v^2}{6}$.
   So $v^2 = 1.5 \times 9.81 \times 6$,
   giving $v = 9.4$ m s^{-1}

10. The base units of $\dfrac{mv^2}{r}$ are kg m^2 s^{-2} m^{-1} = kg m s^{-2}
    $F = ma$ so the base units of F are kg m s^{-2}
    Hence units on both sides of $F = \dfrac{mv^2}{r}$ are the same.

11. $mg = m\omega^2 r$, so $g = \omega^2 r$. Since we want a force of $0.5g$:
    $0.5 \times 9.81 = \omega^2 \times 20$, giving $\omega = 0.495$ rad s^{-1}
    $T = \dfrac{2\pi}{\omega} = 12.7$ s

12. $Mg = \dfrac{mv^2}{r}$, so $v^2 = \dfrac{Mgr}{m}$, so $v = \sqrt{\dfrac{Mgr}{m}}$

13. (a) $\omega = 2\pi \times 6.6 \times 10^{15} = 4.15 \times 10^{16}$ rad s^{-1}
    $v = \omega r = 4.15 \times 10^{16} \times 5.3 \times 10^{-11} = 2.2 \times 10^6$ m s^{-1}
    (b) $F = m\omega^2 r = 9.1 \times 10^{-31} \times (4.15 \times 10^{16})^2 \times 5.3 \times 10^{-11}$
    $= 8.29 \times 10^{-8}$ N

14. 45 km hr^{-1} = 12.5 m s^{-1}. Resolve the reaction force R into vertical and horizontal components:

$R \cos \theta = mg$, and $R \sin \theta = \dfrac{mv^2}{r}$

So $\tan \theta = \dfrac{\sin \theta}{\cos \theta} = \dfrac{v^2}{rg} = 12.52 \div (100 \times 9.81)$

giving so $\theta = 9.2°$

15. In both cases, distance should be on the x-axis. All points on the wheel rotate with the same angular velocity i.e. 4.19 rad s^{-1}. So the graph of angular velocity should be a horizontal line intercepting the y-axis at 4.19 rad s^{-1}. The tangential velocity increases in proportion with the distance from the centre. It increases linearly from 0 at the centre to 104.7 cm s^{-1} at 25 cm fom the centre. So the graph of tangential velocity should be a straight line from (0, 0) to (25, 104.7).

4.4 Simple Harmonic Motion

1. (a) acceleration $= \omega^2 x$, so $0.58 = \omega^2 \times 0.4$ giving $\omega = 1.20$ rad s^{-1}.

   period, $T = \dfrac{2\pi}{T} = \dfrac{2\pi}{1.2} = 5.23$ s

   (b) $x = A \cos \omega t$, so $0.4 = A \cos(0.8 \times 1.2)$, giving $A = 0.7$ m

2. (a) $T = 2\pi \sqrt{\dfrac{m}{k}} = 2\pi \sqrt{\dfrac{0.3}{10}} = 1.09$ s

   (b) $\omega = \dfrac{2\pi}{T} = 5.76$ rad s^{-1}

   acceleration $= \omega^2 x = 5.76^2 \times 5 \times 10^{-2} = 1.66$ m s^{-2}

3. Compare the equation $(0.02 = 0.05 \cos 3.0t)$ with the general equation for displacement, $x = A \cos \omega t$. So:

   (a) amplitude $= 0.05$ m

   (b) period, $T = \dfrac{2\pi}{\omega} = \dfrac{2\pi}{3} = 2.09$ s

   (c) maximum acceleration $= \omega^2 A = 0.45$ m s^{-2}

   Maximum acceleration occurs at the positions of maximum displacement.

4. (a) $T = 2\pi \sqrt{\dfrac{l}{g}}$, so $1.6 = 2\pi \sqrt{\dfrac{l}{9.81}}$, giving $l = 0.64$ m

   (b) $\omega = \dfrac{2\pi}{2} = 3.925$ rad s^{-1}.

   $x = A \cos \omega t = 0.15 \cos(3.93 \times 0.60) = 0.15 \cos(2.36)$

   $x = 0.15 \times \cos(2.36) = -0.11$ m

   (Remember to set your calculator to radian mode.) The pendulum bob is to the left of the rest position as indicated by the minus sign.

5. (a) Amplitude $A = 8$ mm $(8.0 \times 10^{-3}$ m$)$

   (b) $T = 8$ ms $(8 \times 10^{-3}$ s$)$, frequency $f = \dfrac{1}{T} = 125$ Hz

   (c) Maximum speed = maximum gradient of the displacement-time graph $= 6 \times 10^{-3} \div 1 \times 10^{-3} = 6$ m s^{-1}

6. Resultant force, $R = mg = m\omega_2 a$

   When contact is lost, $R = 0$

   $mg = m\omega^2 a$, so: $2 \times 9.81 = 2 \times \omega^2 \times 0.15$

   giving $\omega^2 = 9.81 \div 0.15$, so $\omega = 8.09$ rad s^{-1}

   Frequency $= \dfrac{\omega}{2\pi} = 1.29$ Hz

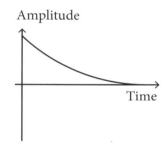

7. (a) Using Hooke's Law, $F = kx$:

   $0.1 \times 9.81 = k \times 2 \times 10^{-2}$, giving $k = 49.0$ N m^{-1}

$T = 2\pi \sqrt{\dfrac{m}{k}} = 2\pi \sqrt{\dfrac{0.1}{49.0}} = 0.28$ s. Frequency $= \dfrac{1}{T} = 3.6$ Hz

   (b) Amplitude $A = 2 \times 10^{-2}$ m.

   $\omega = 22.4$; Acceleration $= \omega^2 A = 10.0$ m s^{-2}

8. $T = 1.5$ s, $x = 12$ cm, $\omega = 1.33\pi$

   (a) $x = 12 \cos(1.33\pi t)$

   (b) $x = 12 \cos(1.33 \times \pi \times 2) = +5.9$ cm ~~below~~ *above* the centre of the oscillation.

9. (a) Period, $T = 20$ s so frequency, $f = \dfrac{1}{T} = 0.05$ Hz

   (b) $\omega = 2\pi f = 0.31$ rad s^{-1}, $x = A \cos(\omega t)$

   $= 8 \cos(031 \times 2) = 8 \cos(0.62)$ giving $x = 6.51$ cm. Remember to set your calculator to radian mode.

10. $T = 2\pi \sqrt{\dfrac{l}{g}}$, so a graph of T (y-axis) against $\sqrt{l}$ produces a straight line graph.

    Once drawn, the gradient gives $\dfrac{2\pi}{\sqrt{g}}$.

    Alternatively $T^2 = 4\pi^2 \dfrac{l}{g}$, so a graph of T^2 (y-axis) against l also produces a straight line graph. In this case, the gradient equals $\dfrac{4\pi^2}{g}$.

11. (a) Damping is a frictional force which results in the amplitude of an oscillation decreasing as energy is being drained from the system to overcome the frictional force.

    (b) (i) Lightly damped:

    Displacement   Amplitude

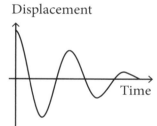

    (ii) Critically damped:

    Displacement

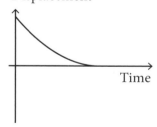

12. (a) The amplitude of oscillation of a mechanical system exposed to a periodic force whose frequency is equal to the natural undamped frequency of the system. The amplitude reaches a maximum value at the resonant frequency. (b) The amplitude at resonance becomes less. The resonance occurs at lower frequencies.

13. (a) 2 oscillations in 4 ms, so period = 2 ms

    Frequency $f = \dfrac{1}{T} = 500$ Hz

    (b) A = amplitude = 0.05 m. ω = angular velocity

    $= \dfrac{2\pi}{\omega} = \dfrac{2\pi}{2 \times 10^{-3}} = 3.14 \times 10^3$ rad s^{-1}

Therefore $x = 0.05 \cos (3.14 \times 10^3 \, t)$

14. (a) Displacement = 0 at positions 2 and 4
(b) Maximum velocity is at positions 2 and 4.
(c) At position, 1 displacement is positive and acceleration is negative. At position 3, displacement is negative and the acceleration is positive.

15. (a) 2.5 m (b) $\omega = 5.0$, so $T = \frac{2\pi}{\omega} = 1.256$ s
Frequency $f = \frac{1}{T} = 0.8$ Hz

(c) $x = 2.5 \cos (5.0 \times 0.1) = 2.5 \cos (0.5)$, giving $x = 2.19$ m (remember to set your calculator to radian mode).

4.5 The Nucleus

1. (a) A = alpha particle source, B = Lead block, C = Thin gold foil, D = Vacuum, E = screen coated with zinc sulfide, F = microscope
(b) The microscope is moved to a certain position and the angle noted. The number of flashes of light seen in a certain period of time is recorded.
(c) To prevent collisions between the alpha-particles and the air molecules.

2.
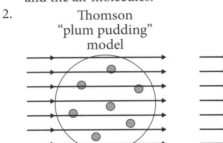
Thomson "plum pudding" model

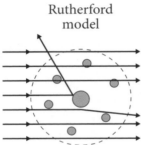
Rutherford model

3. (a) Some alpha-particles were repelled. (b) Some alpha-particles were back scattered, i.e. deflected by more than 90°. (c) Most alpha-particles passed through without any deflection.

4. hydrogen: 1 proton. deuterium: 1 proton and 1 neutron. tritium: 1 proton and 2 neutrons.

5. Cobalt has a mass number A or 27 + 32 = 59 and an atomic number of 27.
Using the usual notation we get $^{59}_{27}\text{Co}$.

6. $r = r_o A^{\frac{1}{3}}$, so plot a graph of r on the y-axis and $A^{\frac{1}{3}}$ on the x-axis. The gradient gives r_o. Alternatively, $r^3 = r_o^3 A$, so plot r^3 on the y-axis and A on the x-axis. In this case, the gradient gives r_o^3. Alternatively, plot $\lg r = \lg r_o + \frac{1}{3} \lg A$, so plot $\lg r$ on the y-axis and $\lg A$ on the x-axis. In this case, the intercept on the y-axis gives $\lg r_o$.

7. Density $\rho = \dfrac{\text{mass}}{\text{volume}} = \dfrac{Am}{\frac{4}{3}\pi r^3} = \dfrac{3Am}{4\pi r^3}$

8. Plot a graph of $\lg r$ (y-axis) against $\lg A$ (x-axis):

Nucleus	^{4}He	^{12}C	^{16}O	^{28}Si	^{32}S
Radius, r / fm	2.08	3.04	3.41	3.92	4.12
$\lg A$	0.60	1.08	1.20	1.45	1.51
$\lg r$	−14.68	−14.52	−14.47	−14.41	−14.39

Nucleus	^{40}Ca	^{51}V	^{59}Co	^{88}Sr
Radius, r / fm	4.54	4.63	4.94	5.34
$\lg A$	1.60	1.71	1.77	1.94
$\lg r$	−14.34	−14.33	−14.31	−14.27

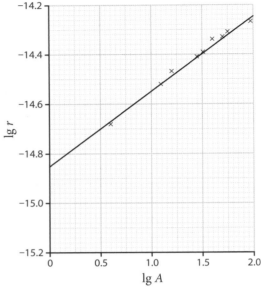

From the graph, y-intercept = $\lg k \approx -14.85$ giving $k = 1.4 \times 10^{-15}$. Gradient = $n = 0.30$.

9. $V = \frac{4}{3}\pi r^3 = \frac{4}{3} \times 3.14 \times (3.04 \times 10^{-15})^3 = 1.18 \times 10^{-43}$ m^3
Density = mass ÷ volume
$= (14 \times 1.67 \times 10^{-27}) \div 1.18 \times 10^{-43} = 1.98 \times 10^{17}$ kg m^{-3}

10. $r = r_o A^{\frac{1}{3}} = 1.2 \times 10^{-15} \times (238)^{\frac{1}{3}} = 7.44 \times 10^{-15}$ m

11. (a) 13 protons and 14 neutrons in the nucleus, and 13 electrons in orbit around the nucleus.
(b) $r = r_o A^{\frac{1}{3}} = 1.2 \times 10^{-15} \times (27)^{\frac{1}{3}} = 3.6 \times 10^{-15}$ m

12. Mass of hydrogen atom
$= 1.008 \times 10^{-3} \div 6.02 \times 10^{23} = 1.67 \times 10^{-27}$ kg
Volume of the nucleus = mass ÷ density
$= 1.67 \times 10^{-27} \div 2.3 \times 10^{17} = 7.28 \times 10^{-45}$ m^3
Volume of a sphere = $\frac{4}{3}\pi r^3 = 7.28 \times 10^{-45}$
giving $r = 1.20 \times 10^{-15}$ m

4.6 Nuclear Decay

1. $^{210}_{84}\text{Po} \longrightarrow \, ^{206}_{82}\text{Pb} + \, ^{4}_{2}\text{He}$

2. (a) Beta-particles are very fast moving **electrons**.
(b) The relative charge of beta particles is **−1**.
(c) Beta-particles can be stopped by a piece of **aluminium** 2 mm thick.

3. (a) $^{42}_{19}\text{K} \longrightarrow \, ^{42}_{20}\text{Ca} + \gamma + \, ^{0}_{-1}\text{e}$

(b) $\lambda = \dfrac{0.693}{t_{\frac{1}{2}}} = 0.693 \div (12 \times 60 \times 60) = 1.60 \times 10^{-5}$ s^{-1}

4. $A = \lambda N$, so: $2.5 \times 10^6 = 2.1 \times 10^{-6} \times N$; $N = 1.19 \times 10^{12}$

5. $t_{\frac{1}{2}} = 1.17$ minutes $= 70.2$ s; $\lambda = \dfrac{0.693}{t_{\frac{1}{2}}} = 9.87 \times 10^{-3}$ s^{-1}
$A = A_0 e^{-\lambda t} = 1000 \times e^{-9.87 \times 10^{-3} \times 50} = 1000 \, e^{-0.4935} = 610$ Bq

6. $t_{\frac{1}{2}} = 51$ days, $\lambda = \dfrac{0.693}{51 \times 86\,400} = 1.57 \times 10^{-7}$ s^{-1}
$A = \lambda N = 1.57 \times 10^{-7} \times 8.0 \times 10^{10} = 12\,560$ Bq

7. $A = A_0 e^{-\lambda t}$. When $t = t_{1/2}$, $A = \frac{1}{2}A_0$, so $\frac{1}{2}A_0 = A_0 e^{-\lambda t_{1/2}}$. Therefore $\frac{1}{2} = e^{-\lambda t_{1/2}}$, and $2 = e^{\lambda t_{1/2}}$. Taking natural logs gives $\ln 2 = \lambda t_{1/2}$, so $\lambda t_{1/2} = 0.693$

8. (a) Number of atoms = $(2.5 \times 10^{-8} \div 0.131) \times 6.02 \times 10^{23}$ = 1.15×10^{17}.

   (b) Decay constant $\lambda = \dfrac{0.693}{8 \times 86\ 400} = 1.00 \times 10^{-6}$ s^{-1}.

   $A = \lambda N = 1.00 \times 10^{-6} \times 1.15 \times 10^{17} = 1.15 \times 10^{11}$ Bq.

9. (a) $\lambda = \dfrac{0.693}{6 \times 3600} = 3.2 \times 10^{-5}$ s^{-1}.

   (b) 140 keV = $140 \times 10^3 \times 1.6 \times 10^{-19} = 2.24 \times 10^{-14}$ J.

   (c) $A = 0.5 \times 10^{-6} \div 2.24 \times 10^{-14} = 2.23 \times 10^7$ gamma rays per second. $A_0 = 6 \times 10^7$ Bq.

   $A = A_0 e^{-\lambda t}$, so $t = (\ln 6 \times 10^7 - \ln 2.23 \times 10^7) \div 3.2 \times 10^{-5}$ = 3.09×10^4 s

10. (a) Remember that the half-life must be converted to seconds. So: $\lambda = \dfrac{0.693}{t_{1/2}} = \dfrac{0.693}{5730 \times 365 \times 86\ 400}$ = 3.84×10^{-12} s^{-1}

    (b) The activity of the source $A = \lambda N$, so N = number of undecayed carbon-14 atoms present **now** = $A \div \lambda = 0.05 \div 3.84 \times 10^{-12} = 1.30 \times 10^{10}$ Remember 3 g is 3.0×10^{-3} kg, so 3 g of carbon contains $3.0 \times 10^{-3} \div 1 \times 10^{12} = 3.0 \times 10^{-15}$ kg of carbon-14. The number of nucleons in a carbon-14 nucleus is 14. So number of carbon-14 atoms = $3.0 \times 10^{-15} \div 14 \times 1.66 \times 10^{-27} = 1.29 \times 10^{11}$ atoms. Activity $A = \lambda N$, so $0.05 = 3.84 \times 10^{-12} N$, giving $N = 1.30 \times 10^{10}$ atoms.

    $N = N_0 e^{-\lambda t}$, so $1.30 \times 10^{10} = 1.29 \times 10^{11} \times e^{-(3.84 \times 10^{-12} t)}$ $e^{-\lambda t} = 0.1008$, so $\ln(e^{-\lambda t}) = \ln(0.1008)$ This gives $t = 5.98 \times 10^{11}$ s (approx. 18 960 years).

11. A = activity in Bq; λ is the decay constant in s^{-1}; N is the number of unstable nuclei.

12. Re-write the equation with mass numbers and, atomic numbers, and hence their neutron numbers:

$$^{238}_{92}\text{U} \xrightarrow{\alpha} {}^{234}_{90}\text{Th} \xrightarrow{\beta} {}^{234}_{91}\text{Pa} \xrightarrow{\beta} {}^{234}_{92}\text{U} \xrightarrow{5\alpha} {}^{214}_{82}\text{Pb}$$

Neutron numbers:

| 146 | 144 | 143 | 142 | 132 |

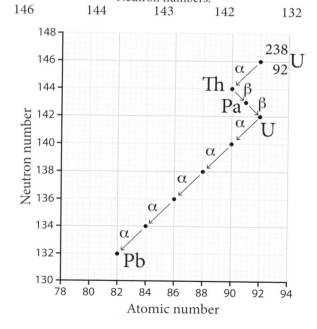

13. (a) $^{131}_{53}\text{I} \longrightarrow {}^{0}_{-1}\text{e} + {}^{131}_{54}\text{Xe}^* \longrightarrow \gamma + {}^{131}_{54}\text{Xe}$

    (b) $\lambda = \dfrac{0.693}{t_{1/2}} = \dfrac{0.693}{8.04 \times 86\ 400} = 9.98 \times 10^{-7}$ s^{-1}

    (c) $A = \lambda N$, so $200 \times 10^6 = 9.98 \times 10^{-7} \times N$ giving $N = 2.00 \times 10^{14}$ nuclei

14. (a) Background is activity from the surroundings. It is measured in the absence of any radioactive source. It is subtracted from the measured activity to produce a corrected count rate or activity.

    (b) $A = A_0 e^{-\lambda t}$. Taking natural logarithms (i.e. to the base e) gives: $\ln A = \ln A_0 - \lambda t$. Note that this is the equation of a straight line. Therefore, plotting time, t on the x-axis and $\ln A$ on the y-axis gives the graph shown opposite. The gradient gives the decay constant. Then, using $t_{1/2} = \dfrac{0.693}{\lambda}$ provides a value for the half-life. The graph shown gives a gradient value of $-\lambda = -9.92 \times 10^{-3}$ s^{-1} giving $t_{1/2} = 69.8$ s (70 s to two significant figures).

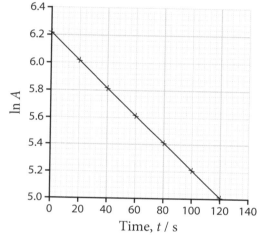

4.7 Nuclear Energy

1. (a) $^{1}_{0}\text{n} + {}^{235}_{92}\text{U} \longrightarrow {}^{141}_{56}\text{Ba} + {}^{92}_{36}\text{Kr} + 3{}^{1}_{0}\text{n}$

   (b) $1.0087 + 235.0439 = 140.9144 + 91.9262 + (3 \times 1.0087) + \text{energy}$ Energy is equivalent to a mass difference, Δm of $236.0526 - 235.8667 = 0.1859$ u Convert the mass difference to kg: $0.1859 \times 1.66 \times 10^{-27} = 3.08594 \times 10^{-28}$ kg Use the Einstein mass-energy equation $E = \Delta m c^2 = 3.08594 \times 10^{-28} \times (3 \times 10^8)^2 = 2.78 \times 10^{-11}$ J To convert this to MeV, remember that 1 MeV = 1.6×10^{-13} J, so $E = 174$ MeV

2. Binding energy in joules = $\Delta m c^2$ = $0.41 \times 1.66 \times 10^{-27} \times (3 \times 10^8)^2 = 6.13 \times 10^{-11}$ J Binding energy in MeV = $6.13 \times 10^{-11} \div 1.6 \times 10^{-13}$ = 382.9 MeV

3. $^{9}_{4}\text{Be}$ nucleus has 4 protons and 5 neutrons. Total mass of the particles that make up the nucleus = $4 \times 1.0073 + 5 \times 1.0087 = 9.0727$ u

Mass difference = 9.0727 – 9.0121 = 0.0606 u
= 0.0606 × 1.66×10⁻²⁷ = 1.006×10⁻²⁸ kg
Use the mass energy equation
$E = \Delta mc^2 = 1.006×10^{-28} × (3×10^8)^2 = 9.054×10^{-12}$ J
Binding energy in MeV
= 9.054×10⁻¹² ÷ 1.6×10⁻¹³ = 56.59 MeV
Binding energy per nucleon = 55.59 ÷ 9 = 6.29 MeV

4.

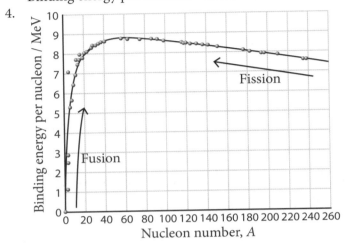

5. The energy release is equivalent to the mass difference between the left-hand side and the right-hand side of the equation. So mass difference
= (2.0141 + 3.0161) – (4.0026 + 1.0087)
= 5.0302 – 5.0113 = 0.0189 u
Energy equivalent = Δmc^2
= 0.0189 × 1.66×10⁻²⁷ × (3×10⁸)² = 2.82×10⁻¹² J
2.82×10⁻¹² ÷ 1.6×10⁻¹³ = 17.63 MeV

6. Stage 1: mass difference = 0.0017u,
Energy release = 2.54×10⁻¹³ J = 1.6 MeV
Stage 2: mass difference = 0.0060u
Energy release = 8.96×10⁻¹³ J = 5.6 MeV
Stage 3: mass difference = 0.0136u
Energy release = 2.03×10⁻¹² J = 12.7 MeV

7. 1 atomic unit mass = 1.66×10⁻²⁷ kg
Energy equivalent (J) = 1.66×10⁻²⁷ × (3×10⁸)²
= 1.494×10⁻¹⁰ J. Energy equivalent (MeV)
= 1.494×10⁻¹⁰ ÷ 1.60×10⁻¹³ = 933.8 MeV

8. 1.008665 – (1.007277 + 0.000549) = 0.000839 u
Mass difference = 0.000839 × 1.66×10⁻²⁷
= 1.3493×10⁻³⁰ kg
Energy equivalent = Δmc^2 = 1.3493×10⁻³⁰ × (3×10⁸)²
= 1.253×10⁻¹³ J = 0.78 MeV

9. Mass difference
= 238.050786 – (234.043583 + 4.002603) = 0.0046 u
Energy release = 0.0046 × 1.66×10⁻²⁷ × (3×10⁸)²
= 6.87×10⁻¹³ J = 4.30 MeV

10. The energy of the gamma rays is equivalent to the mass of the electron plus the mass of the positron.
Mass = 2 × 0.0005486 = 0.0010972 u
= 0.0010972 × 1.66×10⁻²⁷ kg
Energy = Δmc^2 = 1.639×10⁻¹³ J = 1.03 MeV

11. Energy = 1.6×10⁻¹⁹ × 1.5×10³ = 2.40×10⁻¹⁶ J
$E = \Delta mc^2$, so 2.40×10⁻¹⁶ = m × (3×10⁸)²
giving m = 2.67×10⁻³³ kg

% increase in mass = 2.67×10⁻³³ ÷ 9.1×10⁻³¹ = 0.3%

12. Energy = 84×10¹² J. Using Δmc^2 we have:
84×10¹² = m × (3×10⁸)², giving m = 0.00093 kg
(i.e. just less than 1 g of plutonium was converted to energy).

13. E = 210×10¹⁵ J. Using Δmc^2 we have:
210×10¹⁵ = m × (3×10⁸)², giving m = 2.33 kg

4.8 Nuclear Fission and Fusion

1. (a) A **chain reaction** is the process in which neutrons released in nuclear fission produce an additional fission in at least one further nucleus. The neutrons released in the fission of this nucleus go on cause further fissions and the release of more neutrons in turn produces more neutrons, in a repeating process. (b) The reactor must include at least enough fissionable material to reach **critical** size or mass. If the size of the reactor core does not reach this minimum size or mass, then the fission neutrons escape through its surface and the chain reaction is not sustained. (c) Natural uranium contains 0.7% uranium-235 which is readily fissile, and 99.3% uranium-238 which is less readily fissile. The proportion of the uranium-235 has to be increased for uranium to produce a chain reaction in a nuclear reactor. The process by which this occurs is called enrichment.

2. (a) In a nuclear reactor, the moderator is designed to slow down the fast neutrons to the speed of thermal neutrons. The fast neutrons are captured by U-238 which does not fission. The slow neutrons are captured by U-235 which does undergo fission. (b) KE after collision = 0.7 × KE before collision. So: KE after 2ⁿᵈ collision = 0.7 × 0.7 × 1 MeV and: KE after nᵗʰ collision = (0.7)ⁿ × 1 MeV So: 1.0 eV = (0.7)ⁿ × 1.0×10⁶ giving: (0.7)ⁿ = 1 ÷ 10⁶ Therefore: n lg(0.7) = lg(1×10⁻⁶) n × (−0.1549) = −6.0, so n = 38.7. Therefore the answer is 39 collisions.

3. $^{6}_{3}\text{Li} + \boxed{^{1}_{0}}\text{n} \longrightarrow {^{4}_{2}}\text{He} + \boxed{^{3}_{1}}\text{H}$

4. (a) ITER is fusion device that has been designed to investigate nuclear fusion as a large-scale energy source using the fusion of hydrogen isotopes, the same energy source at the heart of stars. (b) A plasma is an ionized gas consisting of positive ions and free electrons. The plasma is heated in a number of ways: 1. An electric current is passed through it and the resistance of the plasma causes heating. 2. A beam of neutral high energy particles fired into the plasma and when they collide with the ions and electrons of the plasma they transfer energy to them. 3. High frequency microwaves are projected into the plasma, which transfers energy to the particles.

5. In inertial containment, powerful laser beams are used to compress and heat the hydrogen isotopes

to the point of fusion. The laser beams are focused on a small spherical pellet containing tiny amounts (micrograms) of deuterium and tritium. The rapid heating makes the outer layer of the target explode outwards. For every action there is an equal and opposite reaction, so the remaining part of the target implodes inwards compressing the fuel inside the pellet and further heating the material at the very centre and results in nuclear fusion. The fusion spreads outward through the cooler, outer regions of the pellet more rapidly than the deuterium and tritium can expand. The plasma is confined by the inertia of its own mass.

6. 1. **Control rods** are to control the fission rate of the uranium. They are composed of chemical elements such as boron and cadmium that are capable of absorbing many neutrons without themselves under going fission. 2. **Concrete containment building** enclosing a nuclear reactor. It is designed, in any emergency, to contain the escape of radioactive steam or gas. 3. The **moderator** is a medium that reduces the speed of fast neutrons, thereby turning them into thermal neutrons which cause fission of uranium-235 so allowing the chain reaction to continue. 4. **Fuel rods** are long metal tub containing pellets of uranium-235, which provide the fuel for the nuclear reactors. Fuel rods are loaded individually into the reactor core. 5. **Steel pressure vessel** enclosing a nuclear reactor which is designed, in any emergency, to contain the escape of radiation to a maximum pressure in the range of 410 to 1400 kPa. 6. The **heat exchanger** passes heat from the gas inside the reactor core system to water, producing steam. This steam then drives turbines to produce electricity.

7. A = (235 + 1) − (141 + 92) = 3
    B = (235 + 1) − (142 + (4 × 1)) = 90
    C = (92 + 0) − (36 + (3 × 0)) = 56
    D = (235 + 1) − (90 + (2 × 1)) = 144

8. (a) Nuclear energy produces less CO_2, a major greenhouse gas, than fossil fuels. It is a suitable replacement for fossil fuels that will eventually run out. However, nuclear energy (from fission) produces large quantities of toxic, radioactive waste and that must be stored safely and securely for between 10 000 years and 240 000 years in order to prevent health and environmental disasters from radioactive contamination. Nuclear reactors can suffer major malfunctions that pollute wide areas. (b) Nuclear power provides employment for the local region, and is a secure source of energy provided the countries that provide the uranium ore have stable governments and societies. Environmental concerns mean many people do not want nuclear power stations near their homes. It is possible to use the same technology to produce nuclear weapons. (c) Many supplies of nuclear fuel are in unstable parts of the world and it may become difficult to source these in the future.

9. Approximately 80% of the energy produced is carried away from the plasma by neutrons which have no electrical charge and are therefore unaffected by magnetic fields. The neutrons will be absorbed by the surrounding walls of the tokamak, transferring their energy to the walls as heat. This heat can be extracted and used to generate electricity.

10. The fission of Uranium 235 yields around 203 MeV of energy. The fusion of deuterium and tritium yields around 17.6 MeV of energy. In fission we have 236 nucleons involved giving an energy release of 203 ÷ 236 = 0.86 MeV per nucleon. In fusion, we have 5 nucleons involved giving an energy release of 17.6 ÷ 5 = 3.52 MeV per nucleon.

11. Energy = $\frac{3}{2}kT$, so $2.3{\times}10^{-14} = \frac{3}{2} \times 1.38{\times}10^{-23}\ T$, giving $T = 1.1{\times}10^9$ K

5.1 and 5.2 Force Fields and Gravitational Fields

1. $F = \frac{Gm_1m_2}{r^2} = (6.67{\times}10^{-11} \times 10 \times 10) \div (0.2)^2$
    $= 1.67{\times}10^{-7}$ N

2. (a) $F = \frac{Gm_1m_2}{r^2}$
    $= (6.67 \times 10^{-11} \times 6.0{\times}10^{24} \times 200) \div (6.4{\times}10^6 + 3.6{\times}10^7)^2$
    $= 44.5$ N
    (b) $g = \frac{F}{m} = 44.5 \div 200 = 0.223$ N kg^{-1}

3. (a) $g = \frac{GM_P}{R^2}$ leads to $M_P = \frac{gR^2}{G}$
    $= ((49.0 \div 5.00) \times (6{\times}10^6)^2) \div 6.67 \times 10^{-11}$
    $= 5.29{\times}10^{24}$ kg
    (b) Density = mass ÷ volume
    $= 5.29{\times}10^{24} \div \frac{4}{3}\pi r^3$
    $= 5.29{\times}10^{24} \div (\frac{4}{3} \times \pi \times (6{\times}10^6)^3) = 5847$ kg m^{-3}

4. Unit for G is N m^2 kg^{-2} = kg m s^{-2} × m^2 kg^{-2}
    = m^3 kg^{-1} s^{-2}

5. (a) $F = \frac{Gm_1m_2}{r^2}$
    $= (6.67{\times}10^{-11} \times 6.0{\times}10^{24} \times 7.3{\times}10^{22}) \div (380{\times}10^6)^2$
    $= 2.02{\times}10^{20}$ N
    (b) $g = \frac{GM_M}{R^2} = (6.67{\times}10^{-11} \times 7.3{\times}10^{22}) \div (1.74{\times}10^6)^2$
    $= 1.61$ N kg^{-1}
    (c) Let the distance between the centre of the Earth and P be D (metres). Then the distance between the centre of the Moon and P is $(3.8{\times}10^8 - D)$. The gravitational force exerted on a 1 kg mass at P by the Earth is numerically equal to the force exerted by the Moon. So, $\frac{Gm_E}{D^2} = \frac{Gm_M}{(3.8 \times 10^8 - D)^2}$.
    Cancelling G and taking the square root gives:
    $\sqrt{6.0{\times}10^{24}} \div D = \sqrt{7.3{\times}10^{22}} \div (3.8{\times}10^8 - D)$
    $D \times \sqrt{7.3{\times}10^{22}} = (3.8{\times}10^8 - D) \times \sqrt{6.0{\times}10^{24}}$
    $2.702{\times}10^{11} \times D = 9.309{\times}10^{20} - 2.449{\times}10^{12} \times D$
    $2.719{\times}10^{12} \times D = 9.309{\times}10^{20}$

$D = 3.42 \times 10^8$ m = 342 Mm (about 90% of the distance to the Moon).

(d)

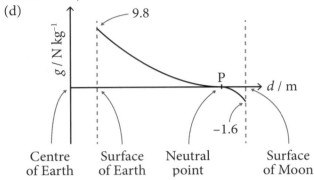

Centre of Earth   Surface of Earth   Neutral point   Surface of Moon

(e) Travelling from the Moon to the Earth, the gravitational force pulling a spacecraft back to the Moon is much less than that pulling it to the Earth and it becomes the dominant force after the spacecraft covers only 10% of the total distance (i.e., to P). Once P is reached no further fuel is required and the gravitational force from the Earth allows the spacecraft to "coast" the remainder of the journey.

6. Centripetal force $= \dfrac{mv^2}{r} = \dfrac{9.11 \times 10^{-31} \times (2.2 \times 10^6)^2}{50 \times 10^{-12}}$
$= 8.82 \times 10^{-8}$ N

Gravitational force $= \dfrac{Gm_1 m_2}{r^2}$

$= \dfrac{6.67 \times 10^{-31} \times 1.67 \times 10^{-27} \times 9.11 \times 10^{-31}}{(50 \times 10^{-12})^2} = 4.06 \times 10^{-47}$ N

So the centripetal force required is more than 10^{39} times greater than the gravitational force. (The electrical force between the positive nucleus and the negative electron actually provides the centripetal force.)

7. $g = \dfrac{GM_P}{R^2}$. For the Earth we have $g_{Earth} = \dfrac{GM_{Earth}}{R^2_{Earth}}$ and for Mars we $g_{Mars} = \dfrac{GM_{Mars}}{R^2_{Mars}}$.

Taking the ratio (the Gs cancel) we have:

$\dfrac{g_{Mars}}{g_{Earth}} = \dfrac{M_{Mars}}{M_{Earth}} \times \dfrac{R^2_{Earth}}{R^2_{Mars}}$.

So, $g_{Mars} = \dfrac{M_{Mars}}{M_{Earth}} \times \left(\dfrac{R_{Earth}}{R_{Mars}}\right)^2 \times g_{Earth}$

$= (1 \div 9.5) \times (6.4 \div 3.4)^2 \times 9.8 = 3.7$ N kg^{-1}

8. (a) Kepler's third law states that $T^2 = kr^3$ where k is a constant. Equating gravitational and centripetal forces gives: $F = mr\omega^2 = \dfrac{GM_s m}{r^2}$, where m is the mass of the planet and M_s is the mass of the Sun. Dividing by m and making the substitution $\omega = \dfrac{2\pi}{T}$ gives:

$r\left(\dfrac{2\pi}{T}\right)^2 = \dfrac{GM_s}{r^2}$. Removing brackets gives:

$\dfrac{4\pi^2 r}{T^2} = \dfrac{GM_s}{r^2}$. Rearranging to make T^2 the subject gives:

$T^2 = \dfrac{4\pi^2}{GM_s} \times r^3$ which is equivalent to Kepler's third law since π, M_s and G are all constants.

(b) $T^2 = \dfrac{4\pi^2}{GM_{Earth}} \times r^3$

$= \dfrac{4\pi^2}{(6.67 \times 10^{-11} \times 5.98 \times 10^{24})} \times (385 \times 10^6)^3 = 5.648 \times 10^{12}$ s^2

So $T = 2.377 \times 10^6$ s ≈ 660 hours = 27.5 days

9. $g = \dfrac{GM_P}{R^2}$. So, compared with the value of g on Earth, doubling the planet's mass will double the value of g. But doubling R will reduce the value of g by a factor of 4. So the value of g on the planet is half that of Earth, i.e. g = 4.9 N kg^{-1} on the planet.

10. Equating gravitational and centripetal forces gives:

$F = \dfrac{mv^2}{r} = \dfrac{GM_s m}{r^2}$. Dividing each side by $\dfrac{m}{r}$ gives:

$v^2 = \dfrac{GM_s}{r}$. Taking the square root gives: $v = \sqrt{\dfrac{GM_s}{r}}$

which is independent of the *planet's* mass (but dependent on the *Sun's* mass).

11. Using an argument similar to that shown for question 8(a) to derive Kepler's third law gives:

$T^2 = \dfrac{4\pi^2}{GM_E} \times r^3$

Hence, $r^3 = \dfrac{GM_E T^2}{4\pi^2}$

$= \dfrac{6.67 \times 10^{-11} \times 6 \times 10^{24} \times (96.2 \times 60)^2}{4\pi^2} = 3.377 \times 10^{20}$

giving $r = 6.964 \times 10^6$ m

So height $h = r - R_E = 6.964 \times 10^6 - 6.40 \times 10^6 = 563$ km (In reality, Sputnik's orbit was quite elliptical and its orbital height ranged from around 215 km to around 939 km.)

12. $T^2 = \dfrac{4\pi^2}{GM_{Galaxy}} \times r^3$. Hence $\dfrac{M_{Galaxy}}{M_{Sun}} = \dfrac{T_{Sun}^2}{T_{Galaxy}^2} \times \dfrac{r_{Galaxy}^3}{r_{Sun}^3}$

$= \left(\dfrac{1}{2 \times 10^8}\right)^2 \times (1.6 \times 10^9)^3 = 1 \times 10^{11}$

These figures are very approximate, but they would suggest that there are, in the Milky Way, stars equivalent to 100 000 000 000 of our Sun.

5.3 Electric Fields

1. $F = \dfrac{1}{4\pi\varepsilon_0} \times \dfrac{Q_1 Q_2}{r^2} = \dfrac{1.6 \times 10^{-19} \times 1.6 \times 10^{-19}}{(4 \times \pi \times 8.9 \times 10^{-12}) \times (50 \times 10^{-12})^2}$
$= 9.16 \times 10^{-8}$ N

2. C^2 N^{-1} m^{-2} = C.C.N^{-1} m^{-1} m^{-1} = C.C.(N m)$^{-1}$ m^{-1}
$=$ C.(C.J^{-1})m^{-1} = C V^{-1} m^{-1}

3. (a) The horizontal components of E cancel, leaving only two components vertically upwards.

$E = 2 \times \dfrac{1}{4\pi\varepsilon_0} \times 2 \times 10^{-3} \times \left(\dfrac{1}{0.5}\right)^2 \times \sin 60° = 124$ MV m^{-1}

(b) Direction is vertically upwards.

$E_{resultant} = 124 \times 10^6$ V m^{-1} = 124×10^6 N C^{-1}. Force on the 1 C charge has the same magnitude as the resultant electric field.

4. (a) A neutral point is one where the electric field intensity is zero. (b) Any charged particle between the point charges will experience two forces, but each will

be in the same direction. So the forces cannot cancel out. (c) $\frac{1}{4\pi\varepsilon_0} \times \frac{Q}{r^2}$ due to +2 mC $= \frac{1}{4\pi\varepsilon_0} \times \frac{Q}{r^2}$ due to the other charge. So: $\frac{2\times10^{-3}}{0.4^2} = \frac{Q}{0.6^2}$

$Q = \frac{2\times10^{-3} \times 0.6^2}{0.4^2} = +4.5$ mC

5. (a) Attractive, because the charges are of opposite sign.
(b) $F = \frac{q_1q_2}{4\pi\varepsilon_0 r^2} = \frac{9\times10^9 \times 40\times10^{-6} \times 50\times10^{-6}}{0.15^2} = 800$ N
(c) Gravitational force $= mg = 0.009 \times 9.81 = 0.0883$ N
Electrical force : Gravitational force
$= 800 \div 0.0883 = 9061$

6. (a) $E = V \div d = 10 \div 0.1 = 100$ V m^{-1} (or 100 N C^{-1}). The direction is vertically downwards. (b) $W = mg$ $= 4.9\times10^{-18} \times 9.8 = 4.8\times10^{-17}$ N (c) Negative. There must be an upward force to balance the downward weight if the oil drop is moving at constant speed upwards. (d) 4.8×10^{-17} N (e) $F = EQ$, so $Q = F \div E$ $= 4.8\times10^{-17} \div 100 = 4.8\times10^{-19}$ C (f) Number of electrons = total charge ÷ charge on 1 electron $= 4.8\times10^{-19} \div 1.6\times10^{-19} = 3$ electron charges. (g) The force has not changed, because the electric field strength is the same everywhere between the plates.

7. $E = \frac{q}{4\pi\varepsilon_0 r^2}$, so $q = E \times 4\pi\varepsilon_0 r^2$
$= 1 \times 4 \times \pi \times 8.9\times10^{-12} \times 0.5^2 = 2.8\times10^{-11}$ C

8. KE of electron $= \frac{1}{2}mv^2 = 0.5 \times 9.11\times10^{-31} \times (5\times10^6)^2$ $= 1.13875\times10^{-17}$ J
Force = energy ÷ distance $= 1.13875\times10^{-17} \div 0.06$ $= 1.89792\times10^{-16}$ N
$E = F \div q = 1.89792\times10^{-16} \div 1.6\times10^{19} = 1186$ N C^{-1}

9. (a) Graph is a straight line through the (0, 0) origin.
(b) E is inversely proportional to r^2 (or E is directly proportional to $\frac{1}{r^2}$)
(c) $Q = E \times r^2 \times 4\pi\varepsilon_0 = 12\ 288 \div 9\times10^9 = 1.37\times10^{-6}$ C

10. (a) Mass of dust particle $= W \div g = 3\times10^{-15} \div 9.81$ $= 3.06\times10^{-16}$ kg
Electric Field $= V \div d = 500 \div 0.1 = 5000$ V m^{-1}
Electrical force $= Eq = 5000 \times (5 \times 1.6\times10^{-19})$ $= 4\times10^{-15}$ N
Resultant force = 4 fN – 3 fN = 1 fN upwards.
Acceleration = resultant force ÷ mass
$= 1\times10^{-15} \div 3.06\times10^{-16} = 3.27$ m s^{-2}
(b) Resultant force = 4 fN + 3 fN = 7 fN downwards
Acceleration = resultant force ÷ mass
$= 7\times10^{-15} \div 3.06\times10^{-16} = 22.88$ m s^{-2}
(c) Since the forces are at right angles to each other, we use Pythagoras' theorem to calculate the resultant force. Resultant force $= (4^2 + 3^2)^{1/2} = 5$ fN.
Acceleration = resultant force ÷ mass
$= 5\times10^{-15} \div 3.06\times10^{-16} = 16.34$ m s^{-2}.

11. (a) E (due to +3 nC) $= \frac{1}{4\pi\varepsilon_0} \times \frac{Q}{r^2}$
$= 9\times10^9 \times (3\times10^{-9} \div 1.4^2) = 13.78$ N C^{-1}
E (due to +2 nC) $= \frac{1}{4\pi\varepsilon_0} \times \frac{Q}{r^2}$

$= 9\times10^9 \times (2\times10^{-9} \div 0.4^2) = 112.5$ N C^{-1}
$E_{Total} = 13.78 + 112.5 = 126.3$ N C^{-1}
Direction: Horizontally to the right.
(b) Difference: Gravitational fields are always attractive; electric fields may be attractive or repulsive. Similarity: Both gravitational and electric fields have an infinite range.

12. Horizontal repulsive force between spheres
$= \frac{1}{4\pi\varepsilon_0} \times \frac{q_1q_2}{r^2} = 9\times10^9 \times \frac{3\times10^{-9} \times 4\times10^{-9}}{0.04^2} = 6.75\times10^{-5}$ N
Suppose the tension in the string is T. Then the horizontal component of T is equal to the repulsive force. So, $T \sin 30° = 6.75\times10^{-5}$ which gives $T = 1.35\times10^{-4}$ N. But the vertical component of T is equal to the weight of sphere A. Weight $= T \cos 30°$ $= 1.35\times10^{-4} \times \cos 30° = 1.17\times10^{-4}$ N

5.4 Capacitors

1. (a) A capacitor consists of two conducting surfaces separated by an insulator (sometimes called a dielectric). (b) For a capacitor of capacitance 12 mF, a charge of 12 mC is required to raise the potential difference across the plates by 1 V.

2. (a) $C = \frac{Q}{V} = \frac{120\times10^{-6}}{12} = 10$ µF
(b) $Q = VC = 470\times10^{-6} \times 50 = 0.0235$ C
(c) $V = \frac{Q}{C} = \frac{150\times10^{-6}}{5\times10^{-6}} = 30$ V
(d) The ratio of the charge stored to voltage across the plates is 2.2×10^{-6}. The manufacturer advises the voltage across the capacitor plates is never allowed to exceed 12 volts, otherwise the insulating material between the plates may break down causing the charge to leak.

3. (a) (i) Arrange all three capacitors in series.
(ii) Arrange two of the capacitors in series. Connect the third capacitor across the series combination.
(iii) Arrange two of the capacitors in parallel. Connect the third capacitor in series with the parallel combination. (b) Construct three arrangements of three capacitors in series. Arrange each of these three series combinations in parallel with each other.

4. $Q = CV = 5\times10^{-6} \times 6 = 3\times10^{-5}$ C
$I = \frac{Q}{t} = \frac{3\times10^{-5}}{60} = 5\times10^{-7}$ A

5. (a) 30 V (b) For 6 mF capacitor: $Q = CV = 0.006 \times 30$ $= 0.18$ C. For 3 mF capacitor: $Q = CV = 0.003 \times 30$ $= 0.09$ C (c) $C = 6$ mF $+ 3$ mF $= 9$ mF

6. (a) For the 2.0 mF capacitor: $W = \frac{1}{2}CV^2$ $= \frac{1}{2} \times 2\times10^{-3} \times 100^2 = 10$ J
For the 1.0 mF capacitor: $W = \frac{1}{2}CV^2$ $= \frac{1}{2} \times 1\times10^{-3} \times 200^2 = 20$ J
(b) $C_{total} = C_1 + C_2 = 2.0 + 1.0 = 3.0$ mF
(c) Charge originally stored in 2.0 mF capacitor $= CV = 2\times10^{-3} \times 100 = 0.2$ C

Charge originally stored in 1.0 mF capacitor
$= CV = 1 \times 10^{-3} \times 200 = 0.2$ C
(d) Total charge stored $= 0.2 + 0.2 = 0.4$ C
Total capacitance $= 3 \times 10^{-3}$ F
New voltage $V = \dfrac{Q}{C} = 0.4 \div 3 \times 10^{-3} = 133$ V
(e) $W = \dfrac{\frac{1}{2}Q^2}{C} = \dfrac{\frac{1}{2} \times 0.4^2}{3 \times 10^{-3}} = 26.7$ J
(f) Original energy stored is 30 mJ. After joining the capacitors together the new energy stored in only 27 mJ. When the capacitors were joined together an electric current flowed from the 1.0 mF capacitor which was at a high potential (200 V) to the 2.0 mF capacitor which was at a lower potential (100 V). This flow of current caused around 3 mJ of heat to be dissipated in the connecting wire by Joule (resistive) heating, so the final energy stored fell from 30 mJ to 27 mJ.

7. (a) Units for RC are ΩF $= (V\,A^{-1}) \times (C\,V^{-1})$
$= (A^{-1}) \times (C) = (A^{-1}) \times (A\,s) = s =$ unit of time
(b)

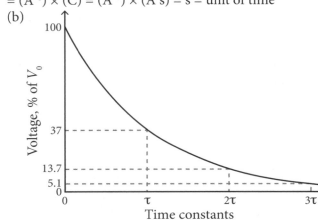

As shown in the graph above, after 1 time constant the voltage across the plates is reduced to 37% of the original voltage, V_0; or $\dfrac{V_0}{e}$. After two time constants it is reduced to 13.7% of the original voltage or $\dfrac{V_0}{e^2}$. After n time constants the voltage is reduced to $\dfrac{V_0}{e^n}$.

(c) (i) $\tau = RC = 5 \times 10^6 \times 10 \times 10^{-6} = 50$ s (ii) $V = V_0 e^{\frac{-t}{\tau}}$ and taking natural logs of both sides gives:
$\ln V = \ln V_0 - \dfrac{t}{\tau}$. Rearranging gives:
$t = \tau \times (\ln V_0 - \ln V) = 50 \times \ln(100 \div 50) = 34.7$ s
(iii) $V = V_0 e^{\frac{-t}{\tau}} = 100 \times e^{\frac{-80}{50}} = 20.2$ V

8. (a)

(b) A stopwatch or timer is also required.
(c) Set up the apparatus as shown in the diagram above. Move the switch momentarily to A to charge the capacitor. Now move the switch to B and simultaneously start the stopwatch. In a previously prepared table, record the voltage, V, displayed on the voltmeter every 20 seconds from $t = 0$ s to about $t = 300$ s.
(d) Plot the graph of $\ln V$ (in V) against time t (in s) and draw the straight line of best fit through the data points. Since $V = V_0 e^{\frac{-t}{\tau}}$, then $\ln V = \ln V_0 - (\dfrac{1}{RC})t$. Determine the gradient from the graph.
From the equation above, the gradient is $-\dfrac{1}{RC}$.
Hence the capacitance $C = \dfrac{-1}{R \times \text{gradient}}$

9. (a) $W = \frac{1}{2}CV^2$, so $100 = \frac{1}{2} \times 50 \times 10^{-6} \times V^2$
giving $V^2 = 4 \times 10^6$ and $V = 2000$ V
(b) $Q = CV = 50 \times 10^{-6} \times 2000 = 0.1$ C
$I_{average} = \dfrac{Q}{t} = \dfrac{0.1}{3} = 0.033$ A
(c) Power = energy $\div$ time $= 100$ J $\div$ 3 s $= 33.3$ W
10. Energy supplied $= Pt = 15\,000 \times 20 \times 10^{-6} = 0.3$ J
$W = \frac{1}{2}CV^2$, so $0.3 = \frac{1}{2} \times 47 \times 10^{-6} \times V^2$
giving $V^2 = 12.766 \times 10^3$ and $V = 113$ V
11. $W = \frac{1}{2}CV^2$, so $144 \times 10^{-6} = \frac{1}{2} \times C \times 12^2$
giving $C = 2 \times 10^{-6}$ F $= 2\ \mu$F $=$ total capacitance of the combination
$\dfrac{1}{C_{total}} = \dfrac{1}{C_1} + \dfrac{1}{C_2} + \dfrac{1}{C_3}$, so $\dfrac{1}{2} = \dfrac{1}{4} + \dfrac{1}{12} + \dfrac{1}{C_3}$
$\dfrac{1}{C_3} = \dfrac{2}{12} = \dfrac{1}{6}$, giving $C_3 = 6\ \mu$F
12. (a) Total capacitance = product $\div$ sum
$= (6 \times 12) \div (6 + 12) = 72 \div 18 = 4$ mF
Charge $Q = VC = 12 \times 4 = 48$ mC $=$ charge stored in *each* capacitor
(b) Consider 6 mF capacitor:
$V = \dfrac{Q}{C} = 48$ mC $\div$ 6 mF $= 8$ V.
Consider 12 mF capacitor:
$V = \dfrac{Q}{C} = 48$ mC $\div$ 12 mF $= 4$ V (Note that the sum of the two voltages is equal to the battery voltage.)

5.5 Magnetic Fields

1. (a) A magnetic field is a region of space in which a moving charge (or an electric current) will experience a force. (b) The field is a series of concentric circles about X, with increasing separation between them and arrows on the field lines in a clockwise direction.
2. (a) The field at A is perpendicular to and out of the plane of the paper – this is usually represented by a dot within a circle. (b) The force is perpendicular to wire 2 and towards the left, that is towards wire 1. (c) The force on wire 1 is perpendicular to wire 1 and towards the right, that is towards wire 2.

3. (a) On AB the force is vertically down. On CD the force is vertically up. There is no force at all on BC (because the field lines are parallel to each other).
(b) Clockwise, when viewed from AD.

4. (a) Field lines between poles of permanent magnet are parallel lines from North to South. Force direction is perpendicular to the plane of the paper, outwards towards the reader.
(b) $F = BIL$, so $B = F \div IL = (0.005) \div (0.5 \times 0.1)$ $= 0.1$ T
(c) There is no force when the field direction is parallel (or anti-parallel) to the direction of the current.

5. (a) $\dfrac{N_P}{N_S} = \dfrac{V_P}{V_S}$, so $N_S = \dfrac{N_P V_S}{V_P} = \dfrac{3000 \times 12}{240} = 150$ turns
(b) Efficiency = Power Out ÷ Power In
$= 60 \div (240 \times 0.26) = 0.96$

6. (a) (i) Maximum flux linkage = BAN
$= 0.0015 \times 0.006 \times 2000 = 0.018$ Wb-turns (ii) E.m.f.
= rate of change of flux linkage = $0.018 \div 0.005 = 3.6$ V
(b) The adjacent sides of each coil will have the same polarity as a consequence of Lenz's Law.

7. (i) Joule heating losses in the coils – by making the wires of both coils as thick as possible and of the lowest possible resistivity, the electrical resistance of the coils is minimised and the amount of heat produced is kept to a minimum. (ii) Eddy current heating in the core – reduced by laminating the core. The laminations increase the resistance of the iron-core thereby increasing the overall resistance to the flow of the eddy currents. So the induced eddy current power loss in the core is reduced. (iii) Loss of magnetic flux – by ensuring the core is a continual loop with no gaps and wrapping one coil on top of the other, flux linkage loss is minimised.

8. $E_{max} = BAN\omega$ and $\Phi_{max} = BAN$
So, $\Phi_{max} = E_{max} \div \omega$
Thus $E_{max} \div 2\pi f = 100\pi \div (2 \times \pi \times 50) = 1$ Wb-turn

9. Induced e.m.f., E = rate of change of flux linkage
$= BAN \div t$. Change in magnetic flux density every
second $= \dfrac{B}{t} = \dfrac{E}{AN} = \dfrac{4200}{1.5 \times 10^{-4} \times 2800} = 10\,000$ T s^{-1}

10. (a) From the definition of the tesla, T = N A^{-1} m^{-1}
= kg m s^{-2} A^{-1} m^{-1} = kg s^{-2} A^{-1}
So Wb s^{-1} = T m^2 s^{-1} = kg s^{-2} A^{-1} m^2 s^{-1} = kg s^{-3} A^{-1} m^2
From the definition of the volt, V = J C^{-1} = N m (As)$^{-1}$
= kg m s^{-2} m A^{-1} s^{-1} = kg m^2 s^{-3} A^{-1}
Hence the volt is equivalent to the Wb s^{-1} since they have the same SI base units.
(b)(i) $\Phi = BAN \cos \theta$
$= 0.200 \times 300 \times 10^{-4} \times 400 \times \cos 60° = 1.2$ Wb-turns
(ii) $T = \dfrac{1}{f} = \dfrac{1}{50}$ s = 20 ms = time to rotate through 360°
Time to rotate through 30° = (20 ÷ 12) ms = 1.67 ms
(iii) When $\theta = 90°$, $\cos \theta = 0$ and the flux linked with the coil is zero. So, from $\theta = 60°$ to $\theta = 90°$, the flux linkage falls from 1.2 Wb-turns to zero. So, the

average rate of change of flux linked with coil
$= -1.2 \div 0.00167 = -719$ Wb s^{-1}
(iv) Average e.m.f. = average rate of change of flux linkage = 719 V

11. (a) *Faraday's Law* states that the magnitude of the induced e.m.f. is equal to the rate of change of magnetic flux linked with a coil. • Connect the terminals of the solenoid to those of the sensitive, centre-zero ammeter. • Plunge the north pole of each of the magnets in turn into the solenoid with (as far as possible) the same speed and observe that the size of the momentary flick on the ammeter increases with the strength of the magnet. For a given speed, the rate of change of flux is directly proportional to the strength of the field around the magnet. • With a given magnet, plunge the north pole into the solenoid with increasing speeds and observe that the faster the magnet the greater the momentary flick on the ammeter and hence the greater the induced current. For a given magnet, the rate of change of flux is directly proportional to its speed on entry to the coil. • Observe that when the magnet is stationary inside the coil, no current is induced because the flux linked with the coil is not changing.

(b) *Lenz's law* states that the direction of the induced e.m.f. is always such as to oppose the change producing it.

• Plunge the north pole of a magnet into the coil and observe the current induced is in such a direction to produce a north pole in the coil at the point of entry, to repel the incoming north pole.

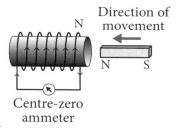
Direction of movement
Centre-zero ammeter

• Now pull the north pole of the magnet out of the coil and observe the current induced is in such a direction to produce a south pole in the coil at the point of exit, to attract the north pole of the bar magnet.

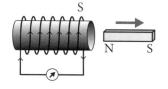

• Now plunge the south pole of the magnet into the coil and observe the current induced is in such a direction to produce a south pole in the coil at the point of entry, to repel the incoming south pole.

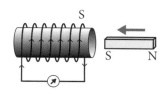

• Finally, pull the south pole of the magnet out of the coil and observe the current induced is in such a direction to produce a north pole in the coil at the point of exit, to attract the south pole of the bar magnet.

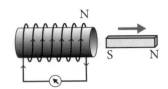

12. (a) E.m.f. $= \dfrac{-\Delta(B \times A \times N)}{\Delta t} = RI = R \times \dfrac{\Delta Q}{\Delta t}$

So: $9 \times \Delta Q = -\Delta BAN = -(-0.9 \times 25 \times 10^{-4} \times 1000)$

and: $\Delta Q = \dfrac{-(-0.9 \times 25 \times 10^{-4} \times 1000)}{9} = 0.25$ C

(b) $<I>$ = average current $= \dfrac{\Delta Q}{\Delta t} = \dfrac{0.25}{5}$
$= 0.05$ A = 50 mA

(c) 50 mA, because the induced current depends on the rate at which B is changing, not on the instantaneous value of B. (d) The direction of the current does not change. Throughout the 5 seconds the magnetic field threading the solenoid is changing at -180 mT s^{-1}. The direction of the induced current depends on whether the magnetic field is increasing or decreasing. Here it is decreasing throughout.

5.6 Deflection of Charged Particles in Electric and Magnetic Fields

1. (a) Force $= Eq = 120 \times (-1.6 \times 10^{-19}) = 1.92 \times 10^{-17}$ N
The direction is opposite to that of the electron's velocity. (b) $a = F \div m = -1.92 \times 10^{-17} \div 9.11 \times 10^{-31}$
$= -2.108 \times 10^{13}$ m s^{-2} (c) $t = (v - u) \div a$
$= -3 \times 10^{6} \div -2.108 \times 10^{13} = 1.423 \times 10^{-7}$ s (d) $S = \frac{1}{2}at^2$
$= 0.5 \times 2.108 \times 10^{13} \times (1.423 \times 10^{-7})^2 = 2.133 \times 10^{-1}$ m
$= 21.3$ cm

2. (a) There is no force on either particle.
(b) $Bev = \dfrac{mv^2}{r}$, so $r = \dfrac{mv}{Be} = \dfrac{1.67 \times 10^{-27} \times 2 \times 10^6}{0.2 \times 1.6 \times 10^{-19}}$
≈ 10.4 cm (1 d.p.)

3. (a) Upper plate is positive, lower plate is negative.
(b) $d = V \div E = 800 \div 10\,000 = 0.080$ m = 80 mm
(c) $F = Eq = 10\,000 \times 1.6 \times 10^{-19} = 1.6 \times 10^{-15}$ N
vertically downwards.
$a = F \div m = 1.6 \times 10^{-15} \div 1.67 \times 10^{-27} = 9.58 \times 10^{11}$ m s^{-2}
vertically downwards.
(d) t = horizontal distance ÷ constant horizontal speed $= 0.120 \div 400\,000 = 3 \times 10^{-7}$ s = 0.3 μs
(e) $s = ut + \frac{1}{2}at^2 = 0 + \frac{1}{2} \times (9.58 \times 10^{11}) \times (3 \times 10^{-7})^2$
$= 4.311 \times 10^{-2}$ m = 43.1 mm
(f) Trajectory is parabolic, towards lower plate.
(g) Horizontal velocity is constant at 4×10^5 ms^{-1}
Vertical velocity = $at = (9.58 \times 10^{11}) \times (3 \times 10^{-7})$
$= 2.87 \times 10^5$ m s^{-1}. By Pythagoras, resultant velocity

$= \sqrt{(4 \times 10^5)^2 + (2.87 \times 10^5)^2} = 4.92 \times 10^5$ m s^{-1}. Angle below horizontal = $\tan^{-1}(2.87 \times 10^5 \div 4 \times 10^5)\} = 35.7°$
(h) • The particle has two independent motions – constant horizontal velocity and accelerated vertical motion. • The trajectory is parabolic.

4. (a) Negative. Explanation: The particles enter the field at a point above the point at which they leave it. Therefore at all points in their semi-circular trajectory (except the point at which they leave the field), the centripetal force has a component which is vertically downwards. Applying Fleming's Left Hand Rule at the point of entry, the force is vertically down and the magnetic field is into the plane of the paper. Therefore the current is horizontal from right to left. But the particles are moving from left to right. Therefore they must be negatively charged. (b) The diameter of the circle is the distance between the point where the particles enter the magnetic field and the point where they leave it. This distance is 40 mm. So the radius, half the diameter, is 20 mm.
(c) $\dfrac{e}{m} = \dfrac{v}{Br} = (5 \times 10^5) \div (1.42 \times 10^{-4} \times 0.02)$
$= 1.76 \times 10^{11}$ C kg^{-1} (d) The particle is an electron. This is because it is negatively charged and has the same charge to mass ratio as the electron.

5. (a) Force is perpendicular to original electron path and to the left. (b) $F = Bev = 0.2 \times 1.6 \times 10^{-19} \times 1 \times 10^{7}$
$= 3.2 \times 10^{-13}$ N (c) Plate on left is negative, plate on right is positive. (d) From part (b) the force was 3.2×10^{-13} N when the electron speed was 10 Mm s^{-1}. Here their speed is 5 Mm s^{-1}, so the magnetic force is halved to 1.6×10^{-13} N. So the electric force to cancel it must also be 1.6×10^{-13} N (e) $E = F \div Q$
$= (1.6 \times 10^{-13}) \div (1.6 \times 10^{-19}) = 1$ MV m^{-1}
$V = Ed = 1 \times 10^6 \times 0.08 = 80\,000$ V
(f) E has units N C^{-1} = kg m s^{-2} A^{-1} s^{-1} = kg m s^{-3} A^{-1}
B has units N A^{-1} m^{-1} = kg m s^{-2} A^{-1} m^{-1} = kg s^{-2} A^{-1}
Therefore $E \div B$ has units m s^{-1}. (g) Those particles with a speed equal to $E \div B$ have electrical and magnetic forces on them of equal magnitude but in opposite directions, so they pass through the apparatus undeflected. Slower particles experience an electric force greater than the magnetic force, and are deflected to the right; faster particles experience an magnetic force greater than the electric force, and are deflected to the left.

6. (a) KE $= qV = 1.6 \times 10^{-19} \times 2000 = 3.2 \times 10^{-16}$ J
$v = (2 \times$ KE $\div m)^{\frac{1}{2}} = (2 \times 3.2 \times 10^{-16} \div 9.11 \times 10^{-31})^{\frac{1}{2}}$
$= 2.65 \times 10^{7}$ m s^{-1} (b) $F = Bev$
$= 0.002 \times 1.6 \times 10^{-19} \times 2.65 \times 10^{7} = 8.48 \times 10^{-15}$ N
(c) $Bev = \dfrac{mv^2}{r}$, so $r = \dfrac{mv}{Be}$
$= (9.11 \times 10^{-31} \times 2.65 \times 10^{7}) \div (0.002 \times 1.6 \times 10^{-19})$
$= 7.54 \times 10^{-2}$ m = 7.54 cm

7. (a) The centripetal force is caused by the electrostatic attraction between the positively charged proton and the negatively charged electron.

(b) 5.33×10^{11} N C^{-1}. The direction of the field is along the radius joining the proton and the electron in a direction **away** from the proton.
(c) $F = EQ = 5.33\times10^{11} \times 1.6\times10^{-19} = 8.52\times10^{-8}$ N
(d) $F = \dfrac{mv^2}{r}$, so $v = \left(\dfrac{Fr}{m}\right)^{1/2}$
$= (8.52\times10^{-8} \times 52\times10^{-12} \div 9.11\times10^{-31})^{1/2} = 2.2\times10^{6}$ m s^{-1}

8. (a) The electrons accumulate on the near side of the conductor. (b) $E = V_{Hall} \div D = 8\times10^{-6} \div 2\times10^{-2}$ $= 4\times10^{-4}$ V m^{-1} (c) $F = Eq = 4\times10^{-4} \times 1.6\times10^{-19}$ $= 6.4\times10^{-23}$ N (d) $F = Bev$ and so $6.4\times10^{-23} = 0.4 \times 1.6\times10^{-19} \times v$ giving $v = 6.4\times10^{-23} \div 6.4\times10^{-20} = 1$ mm s^{-1}

9. (a) Perpendicular component $= v \sin 30°$ $= 2\times10^{6} \times 0.5 = 1\times10^{6}$ m s^{-1}
Parallel component $= v \cos 30° = 2\times10^{6} \times 0.866$ $= 1.732\times10^{6}$ m s^{-1}
(b) $Bev = \dfrac{mv^2}{r}$, so $r = \dfrac{mv}{Be}$
$= (9.11\times10^{-31} \times 1\times10^{6}) \div (0.5 \times 1.6\times10^{-19})$
$= 1.139\times10^{-5}$ m. $T = \dfrac{2\pi r}{v} = 7.15\times10^{-11}$ s ≈ 72 ps
(c) Pitch = distance moved along in one period = speed × time $= 1.732\times10^{6} \times 7.15\times10^{-11}$ $= 12.4\times10^{-5}$ m ≈ 0.12 mm

10. (a) Since the magnetic field provides the centripetal force, $Bev = \dfrac{mv^2}{r}$, so $v = \dfrac{Ber}{m}$.
But, $T = \dfrac{2\pi r}{v} = \dfrac{2\pi r}{v} \div \dfrac{Ber}{m} = \dfrac{2\pi m}{Be}$
(b) $f = \dfrac{1}{T} = \dfrac{Be}{2\pi m}$
$= (1\times10^{-3} \times 1.6\times10^{-19}) \div (2 \times \pi \times 9.11\times10^{-31})$
$= 2.8\times10^{7}$ Hz

11. (a) $Bev = \dfrac{mv^2}{r}$, so $B = \dfrac{mv}{re}$
$= (9.11\times10^{-31} \times 2\times10^{7}) \div (0.18 \times 1.6\times10^{-19})$
$= 6.33\times10^{-4}$ T. (b) Radius slowly decreases. (c) The electron's speed is unchanged because there is no component of the magnetic force parallel to the direction of the velocity (it is always perpendicular to the velocity).

12. (a) The nuclei with the larger mass (the Ba-141 nuclei) travel in the semicircle of larger diameter. (b) From $Bqv = \dfrac{mv^2}{r}$, we get $r = \dfrac{mv}{Be}$ and the diameter $D = 2\dfrac{mv}{Bq}$
Diameter of Ba-141 path $= (2 \times 140.9577 \times 1.66\times10^{-27} \times 2\times10^{5}) \div (0.8 \times 1.60\times10^{-19}) = 0.7312$ m
Diameter of Kr-92 path $= (2 \times 91.9264 \times 1.66\times10^{-27} \times 2\times10^{5}) \div (0.8 \times 1.60\times10^{-19}) = 0.4769$ m
Separation = difference of diameters $= 0.2543$ m ≈ 25.4 cm

5.7 and 5.8 Particle Accelerators and Fundamental Particles

1. • Charged particles accelerated in a closed, evacuated ring. • Particles kept moving in correct direction by electromagnets placed at various locations along the ring. • Direction of magnetic field is such as to produce a force on particles towards the centre of the ring – producing the centripetal force. • The strength of the magnetic field is increased under computer control as the speed of particles increases. • Speed of particles increases in synchronicity with their motion as they pass through an accelerating cavity – the electric field causing charged particles to accelerate. • Particles may be injected in "bunches" or "spills" from a LINAC or a storage ring attached to the synchrotron using a special series of electromagnets. • Particles removed from the synchrotron using a similar electromagnet. • A disadvantage of the synchrotron is that particles continuously lose energy by synchrotron radiation, caused when the direction of very fast charged particles is changed using a magnet.

2. (a) It increases. (b) The accelerating voltage is altered – it is not increased so rapidly because the speed is not increasing so quickly. At speed close to c, it need not be increased at all.

3. (a) Material made up of antiparticles. (b) Pair production in accelerators (like the LHC in CERN). (c) It quickly combines with matter to produce gamma rays.

4. (a) Mass of muon $= 207 \times 9.11\times10^{-31}$ kg $= 1.886\times10^{-28}$ kg. So combined mass of muon and antimuon is $2 \times 1.886\times10^{-28}$ kg $= 3.772\times10^{-28}$ kg.
$\lambda = \dfrac{hc}{E} = (6.63\times10^{-34} \times 3\times10^{8}) \div (3.772\times10^{-28} \times 9\times10^{16})$
$= 5.86\times10^{-15}$ m (b) To conserve momentum.

5. (a) Conservation of both total energy and momentum requires 2 gamma rays to be created.
(b) $\lambda = \dfrac{hc}{E}$
$= (6.63\times10^{-34} \times 3\times10^{8}) \div (9.11\times10^{-31} \times 9\times10^{16})$
$= 2.43\times10^{-12}$ m
(c) Charge, Total Energy and Momentum.

6.

	Force	Approximate range	Gauge boson
Weakest	Gravitation	Infinite	Graviton
↓	Weak Nuclear	1×10^{-18} m	W^0 (or Z) W$^-$ and W$^+$
	Electro-magnetic	Infinite	Photon
Strongest	Strong Nuclear	1×10^{-15} m	Gluon

7. (a) Hadrons are composite particles, whereas leptons are fundamental. Hadrons experience the strong nuclear force, but leptons do not. Hadrons contain quarks, but leptons do not. (b) A baryon consists of three quarks, a meson consists of a quark-antiquark doublet. (c) Proton: uud. Neutron: udd.

(d)

Quark	Symbol	Charge / e	Baryon number, B
up	u	+⅔	⅓
down	d	−⅓	⅓
anti-up	ū	−⅔	−⅓
anti-down	d̄	+⅓	−⅓

(e) None

8. (a) Muon and tau generations. (b) The mass increases.
(c) Antielectron neutrino.

9. (a) quark, antiquark doublet.
(b)

Particle	Structure	Charge / e	Baryon number, B
pi-zero, π^0	u ū	0	0
pi-minus, π^-	d ū	−1	0
pi-plus, π^+	u d̄	+1	0

10. (a) (i) Lepton number on LHS = 1 + (−1) = 0.
Products are not leptons, so lepton number on
RHS = 0. (ii) Electromagnetic – indicated by the
presence of electromagnetic waves. (b) (i) electron
and antielectron-neutrino. (ii) W⁻ particle
(iii) Yes. Consider $^1_0n \longrightarrow\ ^1_1p +\ ^0_{-1}e + \overline{\nu}$.
Lepton number on LHS = 0, lepton number on RHS
= 0 + 1 + (−1) = 0 (iv) Yes. Baryon number on LHS
= Baryon number on RHS = 1. (v) Weak nuclear force.

11. (a) 3. Only the three orbiting electrons are leptons.
(b) 7. Only the 3 protons and 4 neutrons in the
nucleus are baryons. (c) 0. Atoms do not contain
mesons. (d) 10. The nucleus contains 3 protons, each
of which has 2 up-quarks, making 6. The nucleus
contains 4 neutrons, each of which contains 1 up-
quark. So the total is 6 + 4 = 10. (e) The photon
mediates the electromagnetic force. (f) The gluon
mediates the strong force between quarks (but note
that the pion mediates the strong force between
nucleons).

12. (a) Y is uncharged. (b) If Y was a baryon, baryon
number on LHS = 2 and baryon number on RHS =
1. So baryon number would not be conserved. So, Y
is not a baryon. (c) Lepton number on RHS = −1. If a
lepton number is to be conserved, Y must be an anti-
lepton. (d) Y is an uncharged anti-lepton, so Y is an
antineutrino, possibly an antielectron-neutrino.

6A Practical Techniques

1. Typical results:

d / mm	I_1 / mA	I_2 / mA	$\dfrac{I_2}{I_1}$	$\lg_{10}\left[\dfrac{I_2}{I_1} - 1\right]$	$\lg_{10} d$
350	212	303	1.43	−0.37	2.54
450	165	256	1.55	−0.26	2.65
550	135	226	1.67	−0.17	2.74
650	114	205	1.80	−0.10	2.81
750	100	190	1.90	0.04	2.88

Analysis: Rearrange the equation to give $\dfrac{I_2}{I_1} - 1 = \dfrac{k}{R}d^n$

Now take $\log_{10}$ of each side to give:

$$\lg_{10}\left[\dfrac{I_2}{I_1} - 1\right] = \lg_{10}\left[\dfrac{k}{R}\right] + n\lg_{10} d$$

This is now in the form of the equation of a straight
line, $y = mx + c$. So the gradient gives the value of n.
Graph of the above results gives:

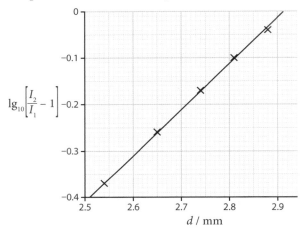

The gradient, $n = 1$ (from the graph). To calculate R,
use the original equation: $\dfrac{I_2}{I_1} = 1 + \dfrac{k}{R}d^n$

$1.55 = 1 + (\dfrac{0.027}{R} \times 450^1)$, giving $R = 22\ \Omega$.

2. Typical results for $H = 2.0$ m are shown in the table
that follows. The values of h should be recorded as
0.400, 0.500 etc to indicate that a metre rule with
1 mm division (0.001 m) has been used. The period
time, T is best determined by timing at least 10
oscillations. In example table below, you can see that
20 oscillations were timed and the average of the three
values was found. From this, the period was found by
dividing the average by 20.

Height, h / m	Measured times / s			Mean period, T /s
	T_{20} /s	T_{20} /s	T_{20} /s	
0.400	50.81	51.11	50.51	2.54
0.500	49.25	49.05	48.95	2.45

0.600	47.44	47.12	47.87	2.37
0.700	45.84	45.54	45.65	2.28
0.800	43.90	43.85	43.75	2.19
1.00	40.05	39.95	40.25	2.00

Analysis: When a square root is present, as in the equation given in this question, it is best to square both sides of the equation. This gives:

$T^2 = \dfrac{4\pi^2}{g}H - \dfrac{4\pi^2}{g}h$. Observe that this is of the form $y = mx + c$. So a graph of T^2 on the y-axis against h on the x-axis will give a straight line. The gradient will give a value for $\dfrac{4\pi^2}{g}$ so g can be found. The intercept will give a value for $\dfrac{4\pi^2}{g}H$ so H can be found. Typical results for T^2 versus h are shown in the following table and the graph that follows.

Height h / m	T^2 / s^2
0.400	6.45
0.500	6.00
0.600	5.62
0.700	5.20
0.800	4.80
1.00	4.00

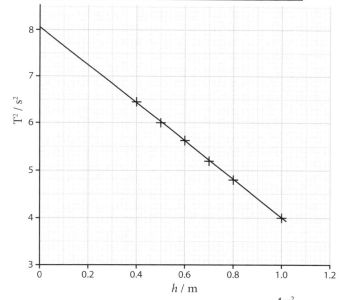

From the graph, gradient = −4.06 s^2 m^{-1}, so $\dfrac{4\pi^2}{g} = 4.06$. Therefore $g = 4\pi^2 \div 4.06 = 9.75$ m s^{-2}.

Intercept on the T^2 axis is 8.05, so $\dfrac{4\pi^2}{g}H = 8.05$

Therefore $H = (8.05 \times 9.75) \div 4\pi^2 = 1.99$ m

3. The following table shows some typical results and how the measurements should be recorded. Notice that units are included with the column headings. Note also that the range of values of D are increased in equal amounts. The D distances are recorded to one decimal place to indicate that a metre rule with 1 mm

(0.1 cm) divisions was used. These values are to 3 significant figures so all the values in the table are also quoted to 3 significant figures.

D / cm	Distance from lamp house to lens / cm		d / cm	D^2 / cm^2	d^2 / cm^2	$(D^2 - d^2)$ / cm^2
	Position 1	Position 2				
65.0	24.0	45.0	21.0	4230	441	3780
70.0	22.0	48.0	26.0	4900	676	4220
75.0	21.0	54.0	33.0	5630	1090	4540
80.0	20.0	60.0	40.0	6400	1600	4800
85.0	19.0	66.0	47.0	7230	2210	5020
90.0	18.0	69.0	51.0	8100	2600	5500

The equation $D^2 - d^2 = 4fD$ is the form of the equation $y = mx + c$ for a straight line graph which has an intercept, c, equal to zero. So a graph of $(D^2 - d^2)$ (y-axis) against D (x-axis) will produce a straight line, the gradient of which gives a value for $4f$. The table above contains extra values to plot this graph. The graph is shown below.

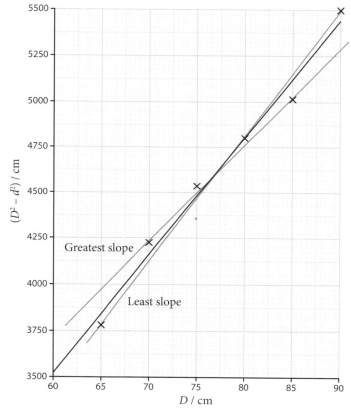

The gradient of the best fit line (shown in black) = 64. The gradient = 4f, so $f = 16$ cm. To obtain the uncertainty in the value of the focal length, two lines one of least slope and one of the highest slope consistent with the data are drawn (shown in grey). The lines of extreme least fit and extreme greatest fit gradient must pass through as many points as possible. When this done, the least value of f is found to be 13 cm and the greatest value of f is found to be 19 cm. This means that the value of the focal length is $f = (16 \pm 3)$ cm.

4. The following table shows some typical results.

Time / s	Expt 1 Current / μA	Expt 2 Current / μA	Mean current / μA	ln(I/μA)
0	10	10	10	2.3
10	8.2	8.0	8.1	2.1
20	6.4	6.6	6.5	1.9
30	5.5	5.4	5.3	1.7
40	4.3	4.3	4.3	1.5
50	3.6	3.4	3.5	1.3
60	2.8	2.8	2.8	1.0

To plot a suitable linear graph to obtain the experimental value of the time constant CR we need to take the natural logarithms (base e) of both sides of the equation: $\ln(I) = \ln(I_0) - \frac{t}{\tau}$. This is now in the form of $y = mx + c$. So $\ln(I)$ is plotted on the y-axis, and t on the x-axis. The gradient is equal to $-\frac{1}{\tau} = -\frac{1}{CR}$. The graph is shown below.

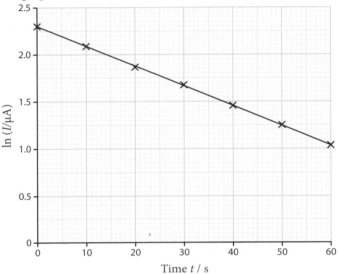

From the graph, the gradient $= -0.021 = -\frac{1}{CR}$
So $CR = 1 \div 0.021 = 47.6$
So $C = 47.6 \div R = 47.6 \div 1.0 \times 10^6 = 47.6$ mF

5. The following table shows some typical results when $R_2 = 150\ \Omega$ and $V_{in} = 10$ V.

R_1 / Ω	V_{out} / V
50.0	2.5
100.	4.0
150.	5.0
200.	5.7
250.	6.3

Formula $V_{out} = \frac{R_1 V_{in}}{R_1 + R_2}$, so: $\frac{V_{out}}{V_{in}} = \frac{R_1}{R_1 + R_2}$

Inverting gives: $\frac{V_{in}}{V_{out}} = \frac{R_1 + R_2}{R_1}$

Dividing both sides by V_{in} gives: $\frac{1}{V_{out}} = \frac{R_1 + R_2}{R_1 V_{in}}$

Therefore: $\frac{1}{V_{out}} = \frac{R_2}{R_1 V_{in}} + \frac{1}{V_{in}}$

So a graph of $\frac{1}{V_{out}}$ (y-axis) against $\frac{1}{R_1}$ (x-axis) will give a straight line.

The gradient is $\frac{R_2}{V_{in}}$ and the y-intercept is $\frac{1}{V_{in}}$.

The new table below, with appropriate headings, shows the quantities to be plotted. All values are quoted to 2 significant figures.

V_{out}^{-1} / V^{-1}	R_1^{-1} / Ω^{-1}
0.40	0.020
0.25	0.010
0.20	0.0070
0.18	0.0050
0.16	0.0040

The corresponding graph is as follows.

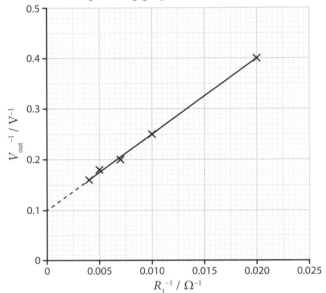

From the graph, intercept $= 0.1$ V^{-1}, giving $V_{in} = 10$ V.

From the graph, gradient $= 15\ \Omega$ V$^{-1} = \frac{R_2}{V_{in}}$.

Since $V_{in} = 10$ V, this gives $R_2 = 150\ \Omega$.

6B Data Analysis

1. (a)

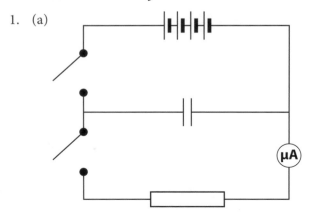

(b) 81.16 µA. Uncertainty = ± 0.01 µA.

(c) Taking natural logs (base e) of both sides, we have the equation of a straight line:

$I = I_0 e^{-\frac{t}{CR}}$, so: $\ln I = \ln I_0 - \frac{t}{CR}$

So we can plot a linear graph of $\ln I$ against t. The y-intercept gives $\ln I_0$ and the gradient gives $\frac{1}{CR}$.

t / s	0	10	20	30	40	50	60
I / µA	75	38	21	12	7	4	2
$\ln$ (I/µA)	4.32	3.64	3.04	2.48	1.95	1.39	0.69

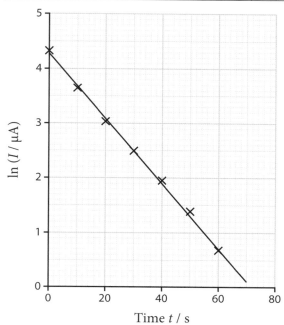

Gradient = $-0.059 = -\frac{1}{CR}$, giving $CR = 16.9$.

We know R, so $C \times 80 \times 10^3 = 16.9$ giving $C = 2.11 \times 10^{-4}$ F = 211 µF.

2. (a)

Lateral deviation, D / mm vs Angle of incidence, i / degrees

(b) See graph in part (a). Remember to draw a smooth curve – do not join the points with short, straight lines.

(c) For $I = 30°$, $D = 0.58 + 0.17 \times 30 + 0.004 \times 30^2$ = 0.58 + 5.1 + 3.6 = 9.3 mm. The difference between the calculated value and the measured value = 10.0 – 9.3 = 0.7 m. Percentage difference = 0.7 × 100 ÷ 10 = 7%.

For $I = 60°$, $D = 0.58 + 0.17 \times 60 + 0.004 \times 60^2$ = 0.58 + 10.2 + 14.4 = 25.2 mm. The difference between the calculated value and the measured value = 25 – 25.2 = 0.2 m. Percentage difference = 0.2 × 100 ÷ 25 = 0.8%.

3. (a) The time interval between each peak remains constant at 0.8 s. (b) Frequency = $\frac{1}{T} = \frac{1}{0.8}$ = 1.25 Hz.

(c) Taking natural logs we have: $\ln A = \ln A_0 - bt$ This is the same form as the equation of a straight line $y = mx + c$, so on a graph with $\ln A$ on the y-axis and t on the x-axis, the gradient will give the value of b.

t / s	0	0.8	1.6	2.4	3.2	4.0
A / m	1.0	0.52	0.27	0.14	0.07	0.03
$\ln$ (A/m)	0	−0.65	−1.31	−1.97	−2.66	−3.51

The graph is as follows.

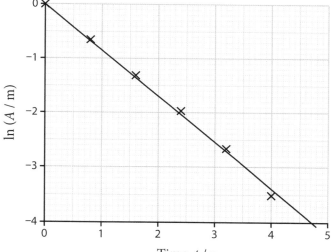

From the graph, b = gradient = $-4 \div 4.7 = -0.851$.

4. (a) (i) $e = 1$ for a perfectly elastic collision (ii) $e = 0$ for a perfectly inelastic collision. (b)

Height H_0/m	0.50	1.00	1.50	2.00	2.50
Total time T_{total} / s	2.83	4.05	5.10	5.75	6.40

(c) A graph of $\lg_{10} T_{total}$ (y-axis) against $\lg_{10} H_0$ (x-axis) will give a straight line. The gradient will give S.

$\lg_{10}$ (H_0 / s)	−0.30	0.00	0.18	0.30	0.40
$\lg_{10}$ (T_{total} / m)	0.45	0.61	0.71	0.76	0.81

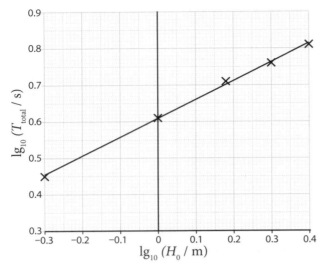

From graph, gradient = $m = 0.51$.

Intercept is the value of y when $x = 0$. From graph, intercept = 0.61.

So: $0.61 = \lg_{10} S$, giving $S = 10^{0.61} = 4.07$

(d) $S = \sqrt{\dfrac{2}{g}} \times \left(\dfrac{1+e}{1-e}\right)$, so $4.07 = 0.45 \times \dfrac{1+e}{1-e}$,

giving: $4.52e = 3.62$, $e = 0.80$.

5. (a) The activity of the long-lived sodium isotope will remain constant. At time = 0 both have the same activity, i.e. 2000 MBq.

Time / s	0	10	20	30	40	50	60
Activity of C isotope / MBq	2000	1400	980	680	480	330	230

(b) $A = A_0 e^{-\lambda t}$, so $\ln A = \ln A_0 - \lambda t$. A graph of $\ln A$ (on the y-axis) against t (x-axis) will be a straight line, where the gradient gives $-\lambda$.

Time / s	0	10	20	30	40	50	60
ln (A / MBq)	7.6	7.2	6.9	6.5	6.1	5.8	5.4

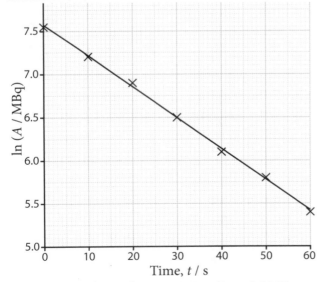

From the graph, gradient = $-2.2 \div 60 = -0.0367$

Gradient = $-$(the decay constant λ), so $\lambda = 0.0367$ s^{-1}

(c) Half-life $t_{\frac{1}{2}} = 0.693 \div \lambda = 0.693 \div 0.0367 = 18.9$ s.

6. (a)

Length L / m	0.200	0.400	0.600	0.800	1.00
Time for 20 oscillations / s	8.00	22.0	42.0	64.0	90.0
T / s	0.4	1.1	2.1	3.2	4.5
L^3 / m^3	0.00800	0.0640	0.216	0.512	1.00
T^2 / s^2	0.160	1.21	4.41	10.2	20.3

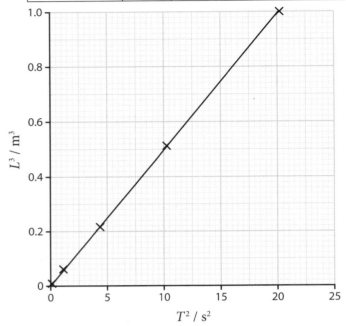

(b) Gradient = $1 \div 20 = 0.05$.

(c) Young modulus

$E = \dfrac{16\pi^2 M}{BD^3} \times$ (gradient of T^2 vs L^3)

$= \dfrac{16\pi^2 \times 0.1}{0.05 \times 0.01^3} \times 0.05 = 1.58 \times 10^8$ Pa

(d) % uncertainty in $M = (0.001 \div 0.1) \times 100 = 1\%$.

% uncertainty in $B = (0.002 \div 0.05) \times 100 = 4\%$.

% uncertainty in $d = (0.002 \div 0.01) \times 100 = 20\%$.

The % uncertainty in d^3 is 3 times that of $d = 60\%$.

Total uncertainty = $60\% + 4\% + 1\% = 65\%$.

Note: The uncertainty in the gradient of the T^2 vs L^3 graph has been ignored.

(e) Young modulus = $(1.58 \pm 1.03) \times 10^7$ Pa.